Run Tall, Run Easy

The Ultimate Guide to Better Running Mechanics

SECOND EDITION

Gerard "GP" Pearlberg

JENNIFER,

RUN TALL, RUN EASY.

BEST WISHES,

COACH GP.

4/28/08

Published by 42K Books, a division of 42K(+) Press, Inc.
Printed in the United States of America.

Library of Congress Cataloging-in-Publication Data
Pearlberg, Gerard.
Run Tall, Run Easy: The Ultimate Guide to Better Running / GP Pearlberg; Foreword by Reed Hastings.
2nd paperback ed.
     p.   cm.

ISBN: 978-0-615-18675-7

1. Running – Training. 2. Exercise. I. Title.

Questions regarding the content of this book should be addressed to
     RunningBuzz.com, LLC
     404 Morgan Parkway
     Brielle, NJ 08730
     www.runningbuzz.com
     e-mail: RunTallRunEasy@RunningBuzz.com

Cover photo: Coach GP Pearlberg works out at a track in Point Pleasant, New Jersey, in preparation for an upcoming competition. Photo by Keith A. Davis Sr.

Photos: © Keith A. Davis Sr.

Editor and project manager: Jan Colarusso Seeley

Design, layout, book cover design: Judy Henderson

Printed by: Dixon Graphics

Dedicated to the heartbeats of my life, my sons, Luke and Sam.

May the Earth forever be gentle beneath your feet,
the waves soothing on your soul, and the breeze a warm
and easy tailwind on your journey through life.

Contents

Foreword by Reed Hastings vi

Preface to the Second Edition viii

Acknowledgments ix

Introduction xii

PART I: THE FAB FOUR **1**

 Chapter 1: Run Tall 3

 Chapter 2: Foot Strike 9

 Chapter 3: Arm Drive 16

 Chapter 4: Breathing 21

PART II: STRENGTH TRAINING SPECIFIC TO RUNNING **33**

 Chapter 5: Getting Started 35

 Chapter 6: Strength-Training Exercises 43
      for Core Stabilization

 Chapter 7: Strength-Training Exercises 60
      for the Upper Body

 Chapter 8: Strength-Training Exercises 77
      for the Lower Body

PART III: THE REST OF YOUR PROGRAM **95**

 Chapter 9: The Fire Within 97

 Chapter 10: Fueling the Fire 107

 Chapter 11: Don't Exercise . . . Train 116

 Chapter 12: Training as an Athlete—True Stories 128

Chapter 13: Reflections of a Coach   141

Chapter 14: Life in the Fast Lane   147

About the Author   157

More Praise for *Run Tall, Run Easy,* Second Edition   158

Run Tall, Run Easy Order Form   159

Coach GP's DVD Order Form   160

Running Notes   161

Foreword

As the founder of the Netflix Corporation, I understand clearly the demands of an ever-evolving marketplace, the requirement for a leader to be able to anticipate these changes, and the needs of an increasingly more informed consumer to be met in a timely and efficient manner.

As a professional running coach, Gerard "GP" Pearlberg faces these same challenges every day and provides first-class service to his athletes around the globe.

GP and I met in Santa Cruz, California, in 1997. My wife, Patty, and I were personal-training with him at the time. Patty was also a member of his all-women's running group, the Iron Maidens. GP would write me weekly training schedules and pace me through grueling track workouts early on Saturday mornings on the bluffs of the UC Santa Cruz campus.

As a businessman, I was impressed with his capacity to adjust his programs to meet the needs of all levels of athletes. His amazing progress with his own running, improving his marathon time by more than two hours over an eight-year period, affords him the unique ability to relate to the novice and elite runner alike.

In the same workout, GP can effortlessly communicate with a runner trying to break the 10-minute-mile barrier for the first time and with a runner trying to average under six minutes per mile in a marathon, affording each the same respect, discipline, and empathy.

Leadership is about inspiring people to reach beyond their preconceived limits and about teaching them to overcome constant obstacles. To quote one of the great leaders of the 20th century, Sir Winston Churchill:

"Success is the ability to go from one failure to another with no loss of enthusiasm."

GP brings the same passion and enthusiasm for his work and to his athletes each and every day, understanding that failure is part of the makeup for success. While his coaching style and philosophy are a constant mix of fairness and discipline, he remains a student of the sport of running, ever evolving in his knowledge and willingness to experiment with new ideas, with the sole purpose of developing the talent of his athletes in a safe, progressive manner.

In *Run Tall, Run Easy*, Second Edition, you will find a book that reflects GP's ability to convey complex, technical information in a user-friendly, simple way that will have you eager to put your newfound knowledge into immediate application in your very next run.

From running form to strength training and nutrition, this book covers it all in an engaging and informative manner. *Run Tall, Run Easy* will become an invaluable resource for you in your own running journey just as it has in mine.

Reed Hastings
Chairman and CEO
Netflix Corporation

Preface to the Second Edition

Let me warmly welcome you to the second edition of *Run Tall, Run Easy*. If you are a veteran of the first edition, I say, "Welcome back!"

In the chapters to follow, I will attempt to unravel the mysteries of poor biomechanics and show you how to overcome them. I will strive to provide you with sometimes humorous, but always useful, information. I will give you the knowledge that will enable you to return to the kind of playful running you did as a kid—relaxed running with good posture. I will focus on several changes that you can make that will have an immediate and permanent positive impact on your running.

As with my original book, you can expect plenty of simple running-mechanic advice, written in easy to follow terms that are battle tested in the trenches, so to speak.

In my experience as a professional coach, there are certain running ideas and thought processes that may work in the laboratory but may not necessarily stand up to the real-time, real-life challenges on the streets, tracks, and trails.

The information in this book is real, it is simple, and it plain works. How do I know? Because I am a blue-collar type of athlete and coach who honed his craft on the fly, out on those streets, tracks, and trails. I know because the information contained in this book worked for me as a developing competitive runner for 17 years and has worked for the thousands of athletes I have coached over the past 12 years.

For the returning reader, you will find many new features in this second edition, from a brand-new foreword from one of the world's leading entrepreneurs to a complete new set of photographs detailing proper running form in addition to outlining proper positioning during strength training.

This second edition is also packed with new material, including the wrist flick, my special ideas for staying focused to ensure that we get out the door every day, goal setting, easy to follow nutrition advice, and new inspirational stories of two of my athletes, all outlined in a new format and design.

All that is left for me to say is, Run Tall, Run Easy, and enjoy the read!

Coach GP

Acknowledgments

The information in this book has been acquired over many years, and I am still learning more each day. Running is a way of life for me, and as such it has afforded me many wonderful memories and many wonderful friends without whom this book simply would never have happened. These are some of the very important people who have woven the tapestry of my life and to whom I am eternally grateful.

Family: To my sister Nicole and brother-in-law Mason, whose combined wisdom reaches deep into my life and helps me chart the right course at all times. Without their having challenged me to run the New York City Marathon in 1990, this amazing journey would never have begun. To my brother Neil for always believing in me and offering his love, support, and friendship.

To my in-laws, Dennis, Sue, Mike, and Mary Beth, for being so wonderful and helping me keep so grounded. Without you, daily life would be so much harder.

To my nephews, Quinn, Cameron, and Mathew; my nieces, Shea, Catherine, Meghan, and Julianna: I love you guys. And finally, thanks to Mom and Dad for your continued love and support. There have been tough times, but your love for me has never been in doubt.

In New Jersey: To Mike Stehle and Jim Milkowski, for the use of their terrific personal-training studio, the Training Room, allowing me to train and practice what I teach.

To my Jersey Shore Stinger athletes, with a special mention to Tom Schaefer, Jim Duffe, Muzz Laverty, Mike O'Connor, Linda Piff, David Zurheide, Christine Difeo, Steve Ludeking, Lisa Doud, Debbie Byrnes, and all the runners past and present who attend our Saturday-morning track workouts in Point Pleasant Beach.

To my NJ youngsters, the Young Guns: Derek Cardinale, Justin Wheat, Amanda Scheer, Jacquelyn Iacouzzi, Kenny Walsh, Kelsey Johnson, Aedan Nielsen, Claire Nielsen, Alex Maas, and Nick Carter. You make coaching so much fun, and you all have such bright futures ahead of you.

To "Billy the Kid" Kelly: you were a great student and training partner; remember to always make the most of your talent.

Special mention to a special athlete: To Owen Boyle: coaching you through your final two years of high school and seeing you develop into a standout runner with an exemplary work ethic is something I will always cherish. Your being accepted to run at Georgetown was the culmination of our high school work together, but we have much work to be done when you graduate.

To my Shore AC Masters teammates, with special mention to Keith Davis, Pat Dolan, and Bob Andrews: competing at Millrose and Penn Relays with each of you was an absolute rush.

To the Shore Athletic Club of New Jersey and Jersey Shore Running Club, for all that you do to promote the sport of running in the Garden State.

To Dr. Lisa Forzani, for keeping me healthy and on the roads and track.

Finally, to my fellow coaching staff and close friends, Tom Schaefer, John Cancro, and David Zurheide: thank you always for your friendship, support, and invaluable guidance.

In California: To my coaches: Marty Kruger, you helped me become a better runner; Greg Brock, you took a runner with some talent and maximized that talent beyond his wildest dreams. Your time and patience with me, I will always be grateful for; you taught me so much. To my training partners: Danny Gruber, Javier Naranjo, Albert De La Torre, Jose Aispuro, Barb Acosta, Tim Nash, Glenn Seiler, Jimmy Clark. You guys inspired me, trained, sweated, hurt, laughed, raced, and dreamed with me. What a journey it was!

To Michael Lawrence, whose friendship and running advice always steered me down the right path.

To my former Iron Maidens women's running group cocoach, Shan Aguilar Stone, and the athletes: you are the best. Coaching you taught me so much about women's running and about trying to become a better coach.

To Rocky Snyder: for your wonderful friendship over the years and for allowing me to use the Pleasure Point Fitness Center for hundreds of workouts, providing the facility for me to develop and teach my craft both in running and strength training.

To the hundreds of athletes in the Golden State whom I have coached, challenging me to become a better coach and person, and especially to the late Don Gardiner for inspiring me. Don's daily battle reminded me to reach out and overcome every day. I miss you.

To Anne Cooney, whose love and support were essential at a time when I gambled on a switch in careers. Thank you!

To my very first running client and friend, Georgia Hamel, who took a chance on a rookie coach and helped the journey begin.

To the Mizuno Corporation, for all its support over the years, with a special mention to Ron Wayne and Anthony Narcisco.

To the Santa Cruz Track Club and the staff and kids from Soquel and Aptos high schools for letting me share your track for so many years.

Nationwide: To my wonderful manager and friend, Jan Seeley, who works so hard on my behalf in helping me reach audiences around the globe to spread the message of *Run Tall, Run Easy!* She also served as my editor and project manager for this edition. To the friendship of Dick Beardsley, Mark Allen, and Mbarak Hussein, three of the great athletes of all time. To my Olympic athlete and friend, Ronnie Holassie, and Olympic trialist, Khalid Ben Mabarek. Thank you both for allowing me to guide you to your running dreams and aspirations.

To my Stingers worldwide, with special thanks to Jacqueline Mariash, Carol Reeves, Jason Elliott, Jeff Blackwell, Ann Sweat, and Connie Kelley.

Thanks to all my excellent photographic models: Shea, Jackie, Irene, Kathleen, and the Jersey Stingers. Special thanks to my good friend Keith Davis for his excellent work shooting all the photos for the book. Your time and contributions were invaluable.

And thanks to three-time Honolulu Marathon champion Mbarak Hussein for your contributions to this project.

Introduction

In a wonderfully written book called *Racing the Antelope*, by Professor Bernd Heinrich, the reader is challenged to consider the antelope as the ultimate long-distance running machine. Possessing an abundance of grace and effortless athleticism, this animal thrives on its natural instincts of survival and its ability to continue to run as an adult with the same wonderful mechanics that it was blessed with as a fawn.

As a child growing up in England in the late 1960s and 1970s, I lived in a society not yet suffering the affliction of music videos, computers, and video games. My natural instinct after returning home from school was to get outside and play football (soccer). Of course, my parents were trying very hard to get me to do my homework, but who had time for that? So, there I was calling up my friends and arranging very serious games of pickup soccer or hide-and-seek. We would be outside for hours, running around like crazy, having the time of our young lives . . . and in the south of England, it should be added, we played in all types of weather.

Biologically speaking, a child at play represents nature's natural order. It is the method we human beings use to develop our agility, coordination, and awareness of our surroundings.

Of course, the last thing I thought about at 8 years old was that 30 years later I would be writing a book, discussing how as a child playing soccer, I was really developing my sense of movement. Back then all I wanted to do was win the game; go home cold, wet, and happy; then sit down to a great grub up (supper) and tell my dad all about it.

As children, we benefit from not having had to fight gravity for very long. Over a period of years, however, this same fight takes its toll on the body, and as you can see from observing older generations, it contributes to compromised posture.

As children, we physically run around at our maximum height. If we are 4 feet, 2 inches, we play to the height of 4 feet, 2 inches, with our spinal discs evenly spaced, our upper-leg muscles developing and flexible, and our gluteus muscles (buttocks) strong. Also, for the most part (although there are exceptions), active children do not carry excessive amounts of body fat, compared to adults. This means that for many people, their power-to-weight ratios are better at this early stage in their lives than in any subsequent stage. From a runner's perspective in particular, this is not good news.

As runners, whether recreational or competitive, we are inundated with information regarding heart rate training. Indeed, cardiovascular workouts and performance represent a key component to success in any runner's training and racing program. However, there is another component that until now has been largely overlooked: the runner's biomechanical form. As a runner, you may have always suspected this was important, but perhaps didn't know exactly what you could do about it and so let your suspicions pass. But there is something you can do! In fact, as I have discovered through my coaching and my continued research, you can do many things to change and improve the way you run. So it is now my mission, through the writing of this book, to help you improve your running biomechanics so that you are always running to your full ability. We are going to take a look at how you actually run.

In the chapters to come, I will attempt to unravel the mysteries of poor biomechanics and show how they may be overcome. I will strive to provide you with sometimes humorous but always useful information. I will give you the knowledge that will enable you to return to playful running—relaxed running with good posture. I will focus on several changes that you can make that will have an immediate and permanent positive effect on your running.

My Fab Four will become tools you use during every run, but they will also help you get out of difficulties such as fatigue, shortness of breath, and mental anguish.

Remember, as runners, we are "ordinary people doing extraordinary things."

Coach GP's Basic Laws of Running

1. Establish a rhythm.

2. Run under control/within yourself.

3. Establish good biomechanics (foot strike, heel recovery, flight phase, support phase, arm/carriage).

4. Maintain good range of motion and flexibility in the joints and muscles through active isolated stretching.

5. Do not go too fast/far too soon.

6. Establish accurate, obtainable goals.

7. Wear good shoes.

Coach GP's Philosophy of Running

1. Running is the oldest, purest sport known to mankind.

2. No apparatus or machinery is required.

3. It's the anytime, anywhere, put-on-your-shoes-and-head-out-the-door kind of sport, a natural blend of art and science.

4. Running, when performed properly, is poetry in motion. It is the simple task of moving your body across the face of the earth as efficiently and effortlessly as possible.

5. Running brings improved health and quality of life, an endorphin-induced natural high.

PART I

The Fab Four

CHAPTER 1

Run Tall

The older we get, the longer we have been fighting gravity just to remain upright. As can plainly be seen in older generations, this challenge can take its toll over time. In later years, it can single-handedly lead to poor posture, with flexion in the shoulders and rounding in the back. In effect, we'll have gotten closer to the planet.

Runners are prone to the very same phenomenon. The closer we become to the planet relative to our own height, the worse things become in our running form and efficiency. Conversely, the taller we remain relative to our height, the better our body will fare and the more efficient we will be.

Forward Lean

One of the first characteristics in the breakdown of running form is the tendency to lean forward. Why should this be? Well, let's examine this more closely.

There are 206 bones in the human body. These bones are at their most efficient in the fight against gravity when they are perfectly stacked upon one another, much as you would find on a skeletal diagram. Remember as a child, trying to balance mom's broomstick or mop on one finger? It was a fun thing to do and of much annoyance to your poor old mom. When you held the broomstick perpendicular to the ground, very little effort was required to maintain the position (see figure 1.1).

Did you happen to notice how much more energy it took to try to hold that broom in place if the broomstick moved from its upright position and you tried to stop it from hitting the ground?

The same holds true with running. The more forward lean you establish, especially if that lean is established from the waist, the greater the additional stress that will be applied to the area of support and stability (that is,

FIGURE 1.1: The upright position of The Stick is more efficient in fighting the forces of gravity.

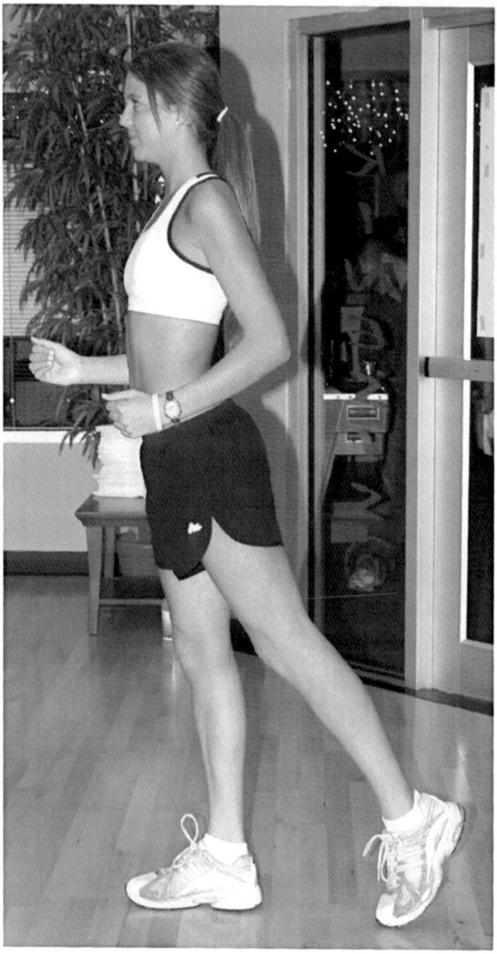

FIGURE 1.2: The proper alignment of the shoulders over the hips and the hips over the lower body.

the low back and pelvic area, the foundation of your torso). When leaning forward, you are basically spending more energy than is necessary during the course of your run. See figure 1.2 for proper body positioning.

Pelvic Rotation

That is not all. If you are leaning forward, you will soon have a second problem to deal with—restricted hip movement. When you lean too far forward, either from the hip or the waist (waist is worse), you will almost certainly experience too much anterior rotation of your pelvis.

To simplify matters, think of the pelvis as a bucket of water. Now imagine holding that bucket of water out in front of you nice and steady. Anterior rotation could be imagined as pouring that bucket of water away from you in a forward fashion (the front of the bucket dropping and the back of the bucket rising closer to you). Conversely, posterior rotation could be imagined as pouring the bucket of water over yourself.

Now, if your hips are in anterior rotation, you are restricting the upper leg's (knee to hip) ability to swing forward and through because your torso is in the way. This then prevents the lower half of the same leg from reaching out and maximizing flight time. By leaning too far forward, you are no longer running to your full height.

Logically speaking, if you're not running to your maximum height, then your hips must be lower than ideal. If your hips are lower than ideal, your body will now have to rise up and over your foot after it lands (see figure 1.3).

During the running cycle, your leg swings through and your foot lands. Then your torso moves over that foot and the foot pushes off, thus starting the cycle all over again. However, if, once the foot lands, the lead or front leg is overly bent and too far out in front of the body, your trunk and hips will sink unnecessarily low before starting the next leg cycle. This causes you to have to "lift up" against gravity at the same time as you are trying to propel your body forward. Consider this: over the course of a 5K race, if you have employed just five centimeters of excess vertical movement per stride, in terms of wasted energy, you will have added the equivalent of a run up a five-story building to the end of your run.

Remember that with too much lean you are already restricting your travel in the air. Not only are you now wasting precious energy in forward motion (through running too low for your height), but you are also not going as far because of restricted leg motion due to anterior rotation of the hips caused by your forward lean. As your form deteriorates, you will go through this "up and over" process using excessive energy and losing

FIGURE 1.3: The inefficient position of the hips being set too low.

ground with each step. If you multiply these two factors by your volume of foot strikes over distance, such as a mile, they become significant indeed.[1]

Shoulders and Arms

If your hips are set too low, your body will naturally compensate through the raising of your shoulders and arms. Basically, your body will be doing its best to raise its center of gravity and your shoulders will be creeping up closer to your ears. If you observe runners as frequently as I do, this trait becomes very easy to spot and is more bad news for the poor old runner. Just why is it that this particular breakdown in form is such a negative? Again, we'll look at this a little further.

Some of the major back muscles that play an integral role in running and forward locomotion are the large latissimus dorsi muscles that sit on either side of the spine. Sometimes referred to as the "wings of the back," these muscles are extremely powerful. The human muscular network tends to work on the big-brother principle, whereby given the opportunity to be engaged, the larger muscles will win out in the fight to perform a given task.

---

[1] Martin, David E., and Peter N. Coe. 1997. *Better Training for Distance Runners*, Second Edition. Champaign, IL: Human Kinetics.

To clarify this point, let's move away from running for a moment and into a gym setting. If a runner is in a gym to perform a strength workout, one of the popular back exercises is the One-Arm Row. This is usually completed with one hand resting on a bench along with the knee of the corresponding side. The other leg stands straight on the floor and slightly out to the side for better balance and a more stable platform from which to lift the weight. The runner will now lift the weight, usually a dumbbell, with the exercising arm. To maximally engage the latissimus dorsi ("lats," or back muscles), thereby strengthening the back, the weight should be lifted in the direction of the hip (see figure 1.4a). However, countless times I have seen this exercise performed incorrectly by athletes, lifting the weight too high up their bodies and more in line with their shoulders (see figure 1.4b). This then almost entirely excludes the much more powerful lat muscles from assisting in the movement and generating power, leaving the task for the much smaller and weaker deltoids (shoulders) to complete.

Why include the explanation of the One-Arm Row exercise at this point? Well, this exercise happens to parallel almost exactly what occurs when we runners raise our arms up too high along our torso and our shoulders creep closer to our ears. We end up losing the sustained power of the large back muscles, replacing it with that of smaller, weaker muscles. These slow-twitch muscles, though enduring, cannot assist as much in locomotion over a long period of time and will restrict our ability to run over distance in a relaxed and efficient manner. So, here are the three things to remember while you are out there running and racing:

1. Keep your hips "neutral."

2. Keep your shoulders over your hips.

3. Keep as much space as possible between your shoulders and your ears.

This leads us to the first of my Fab Four guidelines, specific directions that you can use whenever trouble strikes.

Fab #1 RUN TALL

> At the first sign of fatigue, slowing down, or diminished form, remind yourself to rise from the hips and "run tall."

FIGURE 1.4: Demonstration of (a) correct and (b) incorrect form when performing the One-Arm Row. An exercise ball has been substituted for the bench in this demonstration, but the exercise remains the same.

CHAPTER 2

Foot Strike

One of the greatest aspects of running is its repetitive contact with Mother Earth.

Runners move at several miles per hour, and each second or so, they come into contact with the earth. In turn, Earth moves at several thousand miles per hour through space. Perhaps this unique combination goes some way toward explaining the amazing natural highs and feelings of exhilaration that can occur while we participate in our favorite sport, a sport that is freedom personified.

When running, your ground mechanics (the correct positioning of the lead leg and foot immediately before contact with the ground) play a critical role in the fluidity of forward motion and in the minimizing of impact forces.

Midfoot or Heel Strike?

Under normal running conditions, the only things to come in contact with the ground are our feet, that is, our foot strike, an intricate part of the leg cycle whose importance I cannot overstate. Quite simply, the more efficiently our foot strike is performed, the less time our feet spend on the ground. The less time our feet spend on the ground, the faster we can return the legs to the next leg cycle.

Furthermore, both the location (relative to your center of gravity or body position) and the angle at which your foot strikes the ground have a major impact on your efficiency to propel yourself forward.

The question of forefoot, or midfoot, strike versus heel strike can be somewhat controversial. We'll use a combination of common sense and cold hard facts to find the answer. First, allow me to state with emphasis that for many reasons that we'll discuss, I am a proponent of the forefoot/midfoot strike.

The Shoe Question

Too many coaches throughout the world focus exclusively on the cardio-pulmonary aspects of training, without taking the time at the high school, college, and club levels to actually teach runners how to run. Very often when I address a group of runners, I hear the following very valid question: "If the forefoot/midfoot strike is the proper technique to utilize when running, why is it that shoe manufacturers have focused all of their attention on the support at the heel base of the shoe?"

My answer is twofold. Historically, the mass population of runners have developed poor habits through lack of coaching. Poor technique has resulted in the majority of novice midpack runners evolving as heel strikers. To accommodate this style of running, shoe manufacturers have historically focused on the heel counter of their shoes. I believe that the shoe industry as a whole could have done—and can still do—much more in the educational arena, teaching children how to run properly. The industry could certainly sponsor many more running camps at the high school and club levels. The expense involved would not be prohibitive and could potentially foster long-term loyalty to the generous sponsor. Furthermore, the benefits for our children, along with the long-term prospects for track and field competition in the United States, would be tremendous.

Second, the truth is that shoe manufacturers have in fact begun to pay more attention to midfoot support, cushioning, and stability in recent years.

What's Wrong With the Heel-First Strike?

A child running barefoot in a park or on a beach would not be striking the ground heel first but would in fact be landing on the midfoot, demonstrating simply but clearly that the heel-first strike is not the optimal biomechanical method of running for our bipedal species.

In the previous chapter, we concluded that the taller you remain relative to your own height, the more efficiently and effectively you will be able to run. Now, when landing as a heel striker, you must land with your foot positioned significantly out in front of your body (see figure 2.1). In fact, you land with your front leg bent to such an extent that it forces you to drop your hips. Once again, to propel your body forward, you have to first rise up and over the front foot in order to be able to extend your hip. The result is a constant fight with gravity and a continual waste of precious energy.

Further negative effects are felt by virtue of the angle that your front foot now drives into the ground, causing excessive shock and undue stress up

FIGURE 2.1: The hips are set too low with the lead foot too far out in front of the center of gravity.

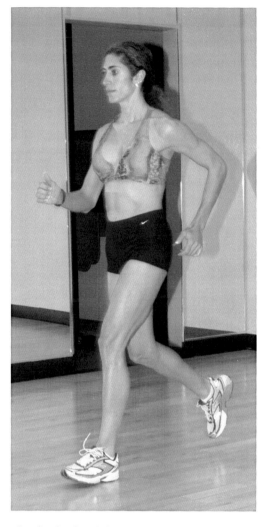

through the lower-leg muscles and knee joints and into the sacral pelvic floor.

The beginning of the next leg cycle is considerably slower than with the midfoot strike since the forward moving torso (carriage) first has to catch up with the front foot before the drive-off leg is in a position to push off. Additionally, the angle of the flexed front foot causes a rollover effect as the runner moves through the heel, to the toe, and then to the push off, slowing down the process even more.

Once the torso (carriage) is in position to be driven forward again by the propulsion of the back leg (due to the fact that the hips are set too low), the back leg again has to drive the hips and upper body up as well as forward. Due to the slow nature of the whole movement, significant drive-off power is lost.

What Happens With the Midfoot Strike?

Alternatively, with the midfoot strike, the support leg is straighter, the torso is moving forward faster, and the drive-off leg action is more powerful (see figure 2.2). The only requirement then is for the hips to be driven forward. When used in conjunction with good arm and powerful leg drives (as will be discussed in chapter 3), the forefoot/midfoot strike provides

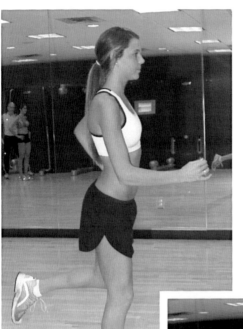

FIGURE 2.2: The proper position of the front foot at the point of contact.

FIGURE 2.3: The proper position of the back foot at the drive-off point (the start of the new leg cycle).

for a faster, smoother running technique that reduces impact forces and allows for better shock absorption (in particular aiding runners with certain preexisting back and knee conditions). It also provides a faster transition back into the leg cycle and creates better posture and a more relaxed running position (see figure 2.3).

Most important, these benefits apply across the board to runners of all shapes and sizes and levels of ability, from featherweight to Clydesdale and from novice to elite.

The Metronome and Heel Recovery

The laws of physics dictate that the closer a weight is to the point of axis, the faster that weight will revolve through space around it. When I was a child learning to play piano, this was demonstrated to me by Mr. Fox, my wiry, gray-haired old stick of a piano teacher. He used a metronome to keep me in tempo.

Simply stated, the metronome is an instrument that works on the pendulum principle, whereby the farther you slide the weight up the scale away from the point of axis, the slower the pendulum will swing, and thus, the slower you are supposed to play in order to keep time, with the reverse applying if the weight is pushed closer to the point of axis. I used to have fun ignoring this particular law of physics, much to the annoyance of Mr. Fox, but that is a whole different story.

Having visited the always useful metronome, you may well ask, "How is this connected to running?" In the biomechanics of running, the point of axis that I am referring to is the hip joint, and the weight is the foot.

At the point of drive off, the more speed you generate, the swifter and more powerful the heel recovery will be (the action of the foot/heel coming up toward the gluteus before swinging back into the flight phase). Therefore, the closer the foot to the hips (that is, the weight to the point of axis), the faster and more efficient this action will be.

Insofar as the principles of physics are related to the mechanics of running, it is critical that you remember the two key factors determining your speed. These are how fast your legs are moving (turnover rate) and the distance you travel with each stride.

Your flight phase (distance traveled in the air) is largely determined by the speed and force generated at drive off and the subsequent speed and efficiency of the leg cycle (the action of the trail leg as it contracts up and swings through to become the lead leg in preparation for the support phase) along with your core strength (see figure 2.4).

FIGURE 2.4: The position of the trail leg relative to the hip/glutes. In our metronome analogy, the foot is the weight and the hips are the point of axis.

With the heel-first strike, the leg is placed out in front of the body, and it simply is not possible to generate the speed and power that can be attained with a midfoot strike. This is because the subsequent drive-off force is compromised and the weight remains farther away from the point of axis through the leg cycle (foot to hip). The result is a slower, less-efficient mode of running.

Conversely, with the midfoot strike, you are landing "tall" and over your center of gravity. The drive-off force generated is faster and more powerful, promoting better heel recovery. This results in faster turnover and increased distance generated in flight, both of which we have identified as critical aspects of faster running.

Conclusion on Heel Recovery

The metronome analogy and its pendulum principle aptly demonstrate the importance of returning the supporting leg—aided by the midfoot strike—into the next leg cycle as quickly as possible, promoting improved heel recovery and generating speed.

This leads us to the second of my Fab Four sequence, the mastering of which will help you tremendously on your journey from the runner you are today to the runner you are trying to become.

Fab #2 FOOT STRIKE

Paying attention to where you strike the ground can significantly improve your running form and counter the effects of fatigue. With the forefoot/midfoot strike, the whole running process is effective, efficient, and fast!

CHAPTER 3

Arm Drive

I hope you will allow me to make the assumption that my readers are interested in improving their running in a forward-moving direction. I am well aware that there are exceptions to this rule, runners who do off-the-wall things, such as circumventing the globe while running backward. If you are a proponent of this style of running, then I would advise you to reverse all the principles that you read in this chapter!

But first this.

A wonderful analogy in the annals of running history is known as the horse and jockey. The idea in the horse and jockey is that your body is composed of two separate entities acting as one. The horse is represented by the lower body, from the hipbones down. The jockey is represented by the torso from the hipbones up.

Imagine, for a moment, that a racehorse could talk. (Work with me here.) With the horse weighing in at 1,000 pounds, it would be most unlikely to ask a 90-pound jockey to assist in providing running power. Instead, the jockey is there to provide rhythm, tempo, and direction. This is true of the runner to a large degree. We must receive our power from our prime movers, which are our lower-body muscles. The carriage (torso) provides stability, balance, rhythm, tempo, and direction. The jockey must be positioned over the horse for optimal synergy, and the carriage must remain atop the lower body with the shoulders properly aligned over the hips. In other words, the jockey must not be in danger of falling off the front or the rear of the horse by leaning too far forward or backward. The jockey should sit with excellent posture: chest up, relaxed shoulders, head level, and arms perfectly synchronized with the horse.

The horse-and-jockey technique can be used in various ways to get out of trouble. For example, by simply focusing on these principles during tough moments in a run, you stay alert, in the present, and in a positive mental state. By adjusting the intensities of arm drive and leg turnover, you can change your workload and gait patterns so that you can actually recruit muscles in a different way. This affords you precious moments of active recovery while you are still in motion.

Become a better jockey, and you will become a better runner. Your racehorse will be particularly appreciative!

The Swimming Pool and the Fighter Jet

From a biomechanical perspective, the jockey is where it all begins in the sport of running. In short, nothing happens until the jockey climbs upon the horse. The success or failure of a run (biomechanically speaking) can be attributed directly to the effectiveness of the runner in producing an adequate and sustained arm drive. If you were standing in a swimming pool chest high in water and thrust your arms behind you, in which direction would you be sent by the resulting force? The answer is forward, of course! Simple enough, but it is amazing how mixed the answers are when I ask a group of runners the same question.

Consider this: a fighter jet at the point of takeoff on an aircraft carrier produces massive amounts of thrust to get airborne from a short runway. In which direction are the engines thrusting their power? The answer, of course, is in the opposite direction of the one in which the jet will be taking off. We are talking about takeoff here, not landing. Thrust produced in any direction other than forward would be problematic indeed.

In physics there is a term known as the hinge moment. There are many examples of hinge moment in athletics. Javelin, hammer, and discus throwing all have their version of hinge moment—which can be understood as the point at which one force ceases and another force continues. One example would be the initiation of flight of a javelin, the hinge moment occurring at the point when the forward movement of the throwing arm stops and the javelin is released.

For runners, a hinge moment occurs when you drive your foot into the ground (see figure 3.1a). Mother Earth says, "No more," and thrusts your foot upward again, returning it to the leg cycle. Your arm movement is in complete unison at all times with the leg of the corresponding side, driving in the opposite direction.

As previously mentioned, in running biomechanics, the second of the two key components is the distance you travel with each stride. Maximal flight time can be achieved only with optimal arm drive (see figure 3.1b), hence the importance of the jockey in running. The fighter-jet and swimming-pool principles are offered here to convey the importance of

a   b

FIGURE 3.1: (a) The beginning of the drive-off phase. Note the excellent symmetry between the left arm and the right leg. (b) Optimal arm and leg drive. Also note the excellent angles of both feet.

counterthrust (arm drive) in providing the runner's ability to produce optimal forward movement.

Arm Drive

As you use force to drive your arm back until it reaches the point at which the chest and shoulder muscles prevent it from traveling any farther, the leg of the corresponding side drives forward carrying the jockey (torso) with it. Thus, the motion of forward running occurs.

An effective way to think of this is in terms of firing a crossbow or bow and arrow. If the bow is drawn back in a mild, timid fashion, the flight of the arrow will be commensurate to it. On the contrary, if the bow is drawn to its fullest extent, the arrow will be shot with power and maximum velocity. This analogy holds true for running. If you drive your arm back in a weak fashion, then your flight time and subsequent leg drive will also be weak.

Of course, common sense has to prevail here. By optimal arm drive, I mean optimal for the distance and pace you are running. Marathoners won't attempt to drive their arms back with the force of a 100-meter sprinter.

The arms should remain close to a 90-degree angle at all times. The downward arm drive of a sprinter may open up to a wider angle to provide more power with a longer lever, but for a distance runner, we are looking for something more efficient. Ninety degrees is the ideal angle, allowing arm levers to remain short enough to move efficiently but long enough to help recruit the all-important latissimus dorsi (back muscles) to assist in generating power (see figure 3.2a).

The hands should remain loose and relaxed, close to the hipbone. If the hands ride high, brushing against the side of the lower ribs, you will compromise the arm's ability to deliver the reverse thrust (like a fighter jet) necessary to assist in generating the desired pace and level of power at which you want to run.

One more point here: it is imperative that the arms not swing across the body. You would not expect a fighter jet to be weaving its way down the runway of an aircraft carrier, so why would you run with your arms moving across your body, wasting precious energy and disrupting the

FIGURE 3.2: (a) The left arm shows the proper angle at the elbow. (b) A perfect front-to-back arm drive, with minimal torso rotation.

smooth flow of air past your body? The less torsional rotation, the better (see figure 3.2b).

Up to this point in the book, all the information relating to good running biomechanics begins with your arm drive. It creates the correct amount of flight time, releases the corresponding leg to reach maximum distance, assists in propelling the torso in such a fashion as to keep you running tall and your hips up, and keeps your torso in correct posture.

This leads us to the third of my Fab Four golden rules designed to optimize your efficiency as a runner.

Fab #3 ARM DRIVE

Think of the arms as the pistons that turn the wheels. If the arm (piston) cadence diminishes, the legs (wheels) will slow down. Maintain a strong arm drive while keeping the shoulders relaxed and you will be able to turn a negative into a positive every time.

CHAPTER 4

Breathing

Over the last three chapters, we have talked a little bit about running biomechanics. All you have to do is run tall, drive your arms, drive off your back foot, develop range of motion in your hip joints, and strike optimally with the forefoot/midfoot strike. Easy, right? Well, maybe not in practice. It can be quite difficult. But nothing worthwhile in life is easy—improved form will pay huge dividends with practice and time.

Now there is one very important topic that we have yet to discuss. All of the preceding advice is not worth the paper on which it is printed without the most important ingredient of all . . . oxygen! After all, in order of priority, how long could we survive without food or water in comparison with O_2?

Many wonderful texts have been written on the subject of cardiopulmonary training. These offer differing opinions and facts related to methods of developing yourself as a runner, in particular, the methods used to propel yourself into peak racing shape. These texts notwithstanding, we are going to examine the subject of oxygen from a slightly different angle, since we'll be looking at how it relates to running biomechanics.

Runners come in wildly differing ages, sizes, and abilities. Nevertheless, one common golden thread weaves its way through the tapestry of running and that thread is relaxation. Let's go through the tools we need to run relaxed.

Breathing and Control

Imagine for a moment a young violinist making her debut at Carnegie Hall with the New York Philharmonic Orchestra, a violinist who will have the honor of performing a solo piece during her very first symphony.

The evening has arrived, and the moment has come for her to play her piece. Some 2,500 people are in the audience, and her entire family has come to witness the momentous occasion. Her adrenaline is racing, her heart is pumping seemingly out of control, and her breathing is frenetic and short. She stares the conductor down as his arms wave enthusiastically, driving the symphony onward. In a flash, he gives her the cue she has been waiting for, and instantly she is on her feet, staring out into the darkness that is her audience.

The point here is that no matter how much adrenaline our violinist is experiencing, no matter how fast her heart is beating, the symphony has its own specific rhythm and required tempo. The music must be played harmoniously and in tune. If her adrenaline gets the better of her and she plays too fast, no matter how talented a violinist she is, her music will sound grating and out of control.

For our violinist to succeed, she cannot rely on talent alone! Her talent must be combined with her experience, her hours of training, and in particular, her ability to master her adrenaline through the control of her breathing cadence. In so doing, she will fill the hall to the rafters with eloquent, melodic sounds.

To achieve success in running at any level, runners too must combine their abilities with complete awareness and control of their body's natural breathing cadence.

Getting Out of Trouble

When you run, most of the time your breathing cadence is hidden away deep in your subconscious. However, when you are conscious of your cadence, it becomes a very powerful tool to be used when attempting to get out of trouble on your run.

At speaking engagements, I am always amazed how few runners are aware they even have a cadence. Once when I was addressing several hundred runners at an expo for the Silicon Valley Marathon, I asked them the question, "How many runners here are aware of your breathing cadence when you run?" Less than a handful answered in the affirmative. This to me is somewhat akin to driving across the country with no provisions or contingency plans in the event that you encounter difficulty. It is leaving everything to chance.

When I am running, most of the time I am on autopilot, especially on my easy days. Nevertheless, there are times, even on these easy runs, when they become a slog, this slog factor being magnified during fartlek training, tempo runs, hill runs, hill repeats, track workouts, or races. When we are running, situations can arise where our breathing gets away from us. Unless we can immediately get it back under control, the prospects for the rest of that particular run or race are not good.

If, for example, you come alongside runners late in a race and hear erratic, out-of-control breathing, chances are they are easy prey for you as you strive to move ahead. On the other hand, if they are breathing smoothly and running to a cadence, watch out, you have legitimate players on your hands.

If you experience difficulty during any of the previously mentioned types of runs, remember to stand tall, keep your hips up, drop your shoulders, relax your belly, extend your chest, and contract your midback muscles to open up the chest wall. Keep your head neutral, your chin tucked in, and your pelvis neutral. (If you take your pelvis into anterior rotation, you will limit the hip flexors' ability to function properly, through contraction and relaxation. Doing this will limit their range of motion, which will then shorten your flight time, so negating precious extra milliseconds of relaxation. This will in turn increase the rate at which you swing your arms—the jockey—driving your heart rate up unnecessarily and affecting your ability to relax. This will create more negative thoughts in your head, and the whole vicious cycle will continue.)

Once you have your body in the correct postural position, it is imperative to quickly regroup and reestablish your breathing rhythm. There are many cadences that can be used, which I will come to in a moment.

Breathing Cadence

The question of how to breathe in and out is one that I am frequently asked at talks I give to runners all over the country. First of all, it is important to tell you that research has shown that less than 40 percent of a person's oxygen intake can be achieved through the nasal passages. When running, you must breathe in and breathe out through both nose and mouth and circulate as much air as you can. If you can breathe in and out through anywhere else, do that too!

Our cardiopulmonary processes are extremely complex, and I am certainly not qualified to try to explain the processes of gaseous exchanges that take place within the body. If you are interested in detailed scientific information on this subject, then I refer you to the chapter titled "Heart, Lung, and Blood Adaptations to Running" found in Martin and Coe's *Better Training for Distance Runners*, Second Edition.

When running, your body naturally falls into a certain running/breathing cadence. Often, you will find that you are striking the ground on one side or another in conjunction with the exhale phase.

As I previously suggested, on most of your runs you may not be thinking or even be conscious of such a cadence. This is fine, but it is essential to know what your natural cadence is so that you can turn inward to it in times of trouble.

Such times (as previously alluded to) may come during intense intervals, during a track workout, during a race, running uphill, running in extreme temperatures or wind, or chasing after the last bus home.

During these times that almost all runners have experienced or will experience, your mind might be saying something like, "I want to stop. I want to sit down. I want to quit. I want to take up a different sport. I will never do this again. Just let the pain stop." Sound familiar?

Well, I cannot guarantee the pain will go away, but I do have some good suggestions to help you focus, relax, and to some extent take your mind off the pain. I hope this will also keep you sufficiently mentally busy to help you cross the finish line in triumph.

It's time to examine breathing cadence more closely. First, I will cover some of the available options, and then I will focus on two that can easily be adopted by all runners and, more important, can be used with a great deal of success.

Cadence Options

3 to 3

Using this cadence, you would take three strides while you breathe in (left, right, left, for example) and three strides while you breathe out. This cadence can be used at a slow running pace, either for a warm-up, perhaps, or for a beginning runner.

3 to 2

Using this cadence, you would take three strides while breathing in and two while breathing out. It can be used at a slightly faster pace. This can be effective during an easy-paced, longer-run effort: faster than a warm-up but not as fast as a track workout or tempo run.

2 to 1

For a faster type tempo run or perhaps even a 10K or 10-mile race pace, you might choose a 2 to 1 cadence. Again, this would be two strides while you breathe in and one while you breathe out.

The two easily adoptable cadences to which I have previously referred are as follows.

3 to 1

In this cadence you inhale smoothly over three steps followed by a short forceful exhale or out-breath over one step (most commonly the right side—believed to be connected to the diaphragm). So you breathe in on left, in on right, and in on next left, and then breathe *out* on the next right foot strike. Repeat the sequence.

I like this tempo as a very versatile cadence that can be utilized all the way from the warm-up to perhaps even 5K race pace for a very fit individual (at least for the first half of the race).

2 to 2

This cadence involves breathing in for two strides and breathing out for two strides, very symmetrically and very rhythmically and efficiently, giving you a chance for a longer exhale. It is most effective during certain longer-interval track workouts or hill repeats. This is a common cadence, particularly at a faster pace (half-mile race pace perhaps to 5K pace).

Note: A 1-to-1 ratio is an option that may be used only at the end of a race in a frenetic sprint to the line from approximately 300 to 400 meters out. If you find yourself breathing in a 1-to-1 ratio, you are at the point of maximal energy expenditure. If you are in the first mile of a marathon and a person running next to you is using a 1-to-1 ratio, do not expect that person to be around very long in the race!

What Cadence Is Best on Hills?

I touched on hills a moment ago, both in running hills and hill repeats (wind sprints up a hill). This requires a shorter stride pattern and an increase in stride frequency. Your breathing rate increases accordingly, depending on the pace you are running. A 2-to-2 cadence may be a very powerful weapon for you on those hills. Try it, and see for yourself.

Practice and experiment with cadences in your training. Once you have mastered them, tuck them away in your physiological arsenal, and pull them out at opportune moments in your running and racing. Using these cadences will help you to regroup, refocus, and most important of all, relax in your run. (Run Easy!)

My Defining Run

One cool winter's evening while I was running solo adjacent to the Pacific Ocean along West Cliff Drive in Santa Cruz, California, in the early 1990s, I became aware of something that would ultimately contribute significantly to my development as a runner. I refer to this discovery as my secret weapon.

I am not a scientist. I do not even have a degree in physiology. My education as a running coach was not cultivated in the classroom or in the laboratory but rather as an experiment of one out in the trenches: running, an education that enabled me to improve my marathon time by over two hours to 2:34 and my mile time to within 40 seconds of the world record over an eight-year span between age 27 and age 35. It was learned in the best school of all, the school of hard knocks.

On that cool evening, I became very aware of the cause and effect of the arm cadence. The slightest change in rhythm of the arm movement dictated a change in running speed. The arms, in my mind, were akin to a stick shift in a car. Change gears up or down with the arms, and the rest of the body would react by decelerating or accelerating.

As my curiosity increased with each passing moment, I zoned in a little further to the whole rhythm and timing aspect. Breath, *wrist*, foot strike. What was that? Wrist? I asked myself, what had I seen? What had I noticed? Wrist? I discovered on this night, a night of pure poetry in motion, all systems firing in harmony, that these three key elements happened simultaneously:

1. My left foot struck the ground on the midfoot just ahead of my center of gravity.

2. At the exact moment that my left foot made contact with the ground, my left arm reached the lowest point of its arm swing (with, most significantly, the wrist flicking upward in a powerful yet relaxed movement forward) directly over the left ankle.

3. As these two movements occurred, they happened at the exact moment that I needed to breathe out.

These three things occur simultaneously when I am running at my very best, not related to pace—just in a rhythm, a rhythm that can take place equally at slow or fast speeds. When one or more of these things are out of sync, then I am out of sync.

There were references in the past to the legendary basketball player, Michael Jordan, finding a zone so powerful that he could shoot free throws with his eyes closed. Let's assume that there would be occasional days when Michael Jordan was not in the zone and attempted to shoot free throws with his eyes closed and missed. He still knew the mechanics and essentials of the movement. Nothing changed except the intangible of the zone. He could attempt to consciously make the adjustments, but it may not mean that he would make the baskets that day. What was more important was that he understood the mechanics; he knew his body, his mind, and his touch; and if he applied the biomechanical principles hard-wired into him, the "zone" would come. Understanding the process was the key for him.

This is the case for my own self-discovery. If you are having a tough running day, and if running technique is that simple, why not make an adjustment if you find one of the three things out of sync to reestablish your rhythm?

This is a great question and a reasonable thought process. However, I have come to know over the years that just as Michael Jordan could make conscious adjustments and still not meet with success on that particular day, so it goes with our running. It is not for the lack of trying. I indeed do attempt, as the question suggests, to make conscious adjustments to turn a painful run into a painless one, but alas, it is not always that easy.

I am breaking running form down to as simple a notion as possible, but there are an infinite number of other factors, of which we perhaps will never be aware, that on a given day prevent us from being comfortable.

However, a better understanding of the mechanics, the movements, and the very elements of timing that generate our forward locomotion may provide no guarantees, but at the very least it contributes to increasing the odds in our favor of

1. salvaging a bad run,
2. sustaining a good run,
3. identifying and recognizing our running in a zone, and
4. opening the door to our becoming significantly better runners.

The Wrist Flick

If these three elements—breath, wrist flick, and foot strike—formulate my secret weapon, then the character that plays the starring role in this discovery is the wrist flick. It's an easily overlooked, innocuous element of our arm movement that, when identified and mastered, opens the door to the possibility of a complete change of running form and increase in relaxation.

Contemplate for a moment the act of hammering a nail into a wall. While holding the nail steady with one hand, you draw the other arm back before generating forward movement with the arm/hand holding the hammer. As the forward-moving lower arm reaches a certain point and

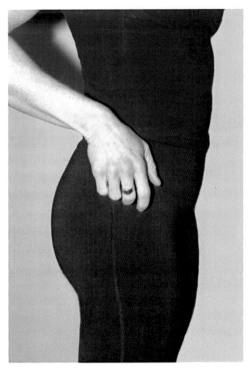

FIGURE 4.1: The proper relaxed, articulated position of the hand. Note the perfect placement of the right thumb.

stops (a hinged moment), an articulated action at the wrist joint would follow, leading to the point of contact between hammer and nail. This instinctive flick of the wrist is what generates force in a relaxed, efficient manner. It also makes the returning of the hammer to its original starting point much easier, with considerable rhythm for the next forward cycle.

So it is with running. As I was running that memorable night, my wrists (as they reached a point with each forward/backward movement adjacent to my hips at the lowest point of the arm cadence, with thumbs placed atop my index fingers) articulated in a flicklike manner that resulted in fluidlike relaxation that emanated all the way up my arms into my torso (see figure 4.1).

I began to believe then, and still believe today, that the wrist flick is the tiny, golden element that forms the linchpin upon which the foundation of proper running is built.

Note to Coaches

Teach your runners, especially the young, the image of the *hammer and the nail,* and you will present them with a powerful visual image that they can use to harness and cultivate the flick in their form that will serve them well in training and races for years to come.

Some runners have excessive cross rotation, a style of running that I affectionately call "driving the bus." In this style, runners inadvertently keep a firm wrist and do not articulate at the joint. Teach them to flick the wrist, and their problems of cross rotating will be solved. Simple as that.

All of this leads us to the last of my favorite techniques for getting out of trouble during a run.

Fab #4 BREATHING

Rhythm and timing are paramount in running. When your rhythm and timing are off, running can be miserable. Early recognition of this situation followed by a swift tune-up (a return to rhythmic cadence with proper breathing technique) can reestablish your sense of timing, relaxation, and calm. Know your breathing rhythm and use it to regain control when trouble starts.

The Story of Joe: A Child No More

The story of Joe is one with which we can easily identify. You see, Joe is the weekend warrior personified: outwardly confident, game for many things. On a challenge from a friend, he has been training for a local 10K for about three weeks. The good news is that he has been training (termed loosely). The bad news is that the 10K is this weekend. He feels that this poses no problem, as many people similarly would. He thinks to himself, *I used to be an athlete in college. How hard could it be to run six miles?*

On the morning of the race, Joe is ready to go. He drives to the start, gets out of his car, lifts his bent leg onto the bumper for a quick hamstring stretch, and does a 60-second warm-up jog. Now, Joe is ready to race, or so he thinks.

Joe is psyched to see that his wife and children are there, along with his friends, none of whom can believe he took up the dare in the first place. He nervously chugs down half a bottle of his favorite sports drink, takes a bite of his friend's energy bar, bobs up and down in an attempt to touch his toes, and awaits the start. The gun goes off, and the race begins.

A half mile into the race, Joe is looking pretty good, except for the fact that he is running one-mile race pace in a 10K, a mistake that will later come back to haunt him. However, that notwithstanding, he is using his entire 5-foot-10-inch frame, is pumping his arms, and has good leg turnover.

Joe had no real time goal before he started but decided early on that he could stay with his daughter's high school math teacher. After all, the teacher's physical presence did not suggest that this would be much of a challenge, although Joe seemed to remember hearing that the teacher fancied himself as a "bit of a runner." This bit of a runner is one of the top masters runners in the area, with a personal best in the 10K of 31 minutes, 40 seconds 15 years earlier and still putting in about 35 to 40 miles per week. On a good day, he can still manage to run a 35-minute 10K.

This error in judgment, magnified by that magic ingredient known as testosterone, is Joe's first mistake. His second is coming through the first mile marker in just under six minutes. Now, to be fair to Joe, running a mile in under six minutes is a very impressive feat indeed—particularly for someone who, apart from the previous few weeks, has run sporadically at best over the prior dozen years. It certainly shows athletic ability.

However, running, as you know, is not a cheater's sport. It gives you nowhere to hide and no way to overcome the laws of both biology and physics. Just past the mile marker, the first chinks in Joe's armor begin to show.

His 5-foot-10-inch frame is now running at 5 feet, 8 inches. He is seemingly getting closer to the planet with every stride. Only minutes before, Joe could overcome his poor biomechanics with adrenaline and fresh legs. His heel-strike inefficiency was temporarily outweighed by an almost cartoonlike rapid rate of leg turnover. Now, however, the effects of his heel driving into the ground and having to continually lift his body up and over his front foot before being able to drive off are beginning to take their toll on his oxygen-delivery system. In other words, he is flat out beginning to tire.

What is happening at the cellular level to hasten the demise of Joe's race? There is a high accumulation of lactic acid as Joe moves beyond his lactate threshold (the point at which lactic acid is being produced faster than it can be removed from the working muscles). It is not too long before metabolic and neuromuscular activity begins to decrease. Joe's pulmonary system is not able to deliver enough oxygen for the demands being placed upon it, and quite simply, his heart is beating too fast to be able to cope.

Biomechanically, Joe's leg drive is beginning to fade by the minute. He is probably close to 100 leg strikes per minute per leg, which is way too high. Ideally, he needs to be in the high 80s to mid-90s, otherwise his stride just isn't covering enough distance, almost akin to running on the spot. Since he is not generating enough force with his drive off, he is now creating almost no lift from his heels, and his feet are swinging through too far from his hips. Just as in the metronome analogy described earlier, the weight is a long way from the point of axis. We know what happens now, right? The levers move at a slower and less-efficient rate, and Joe is going nowhere fast.

Joe's midsection (his abdominal and lower back muscles), not adapted to the stresses of running, start to collapse inwardly, as do his shoulders as he begins to round forward. Now he is fighting gravity in a very inefficient manner, as his skeletal structure is no longer optimally aligned. To add insult to injury, since his shoulders are hunched over, he is now contracting his chest muscles, applying undue pressure on his rib cage. This fact, along with his head being pressed too far down, as he is not strong enough to support it properly (the jockey is falling off the front of the horse), compounds his biggest problem—his inability to get enough air. He is struggling to breathe, and the violinist is completely out of sync with the symphony.

The final link in this sad chain of events, the one that really finishes him off from a biomechanical perspective, is that his arm drive is now weak at best. The same arm drive that just eight minutes before was so decisive, so crisp, and so bold, has now fizzled to a feeble gesture that barely extends behind his torso. His arms are now somewhere up around his midrib area, with hardly any counter-rotational force being generated (that crossbow hardly being drawn at all). With his corresponding leg, there is no drive, no lift, no flight, and ultimately no Joe in the race. He is beaten by ego initially, and along with his poor cardiopulmonary conditioning, his ultimate defeat comes from very poor biomechanics. Joe's day in this race is over! Against his name in the finishing results, those infamous letters: Joe . . . DNF.

Contributing to the richness of our sport is the fact that there is nowhere to hide. Running exposes all those who dare to take shortcuts. Next time you are at a local running race, whether you are competing or cheering, look out for Joe. He will be there; he always is. Long live Joe, as he serves as a very keen reminder of the way not to do things when it comes to the sport of running, or come to think of it, anything else in life. ■

Strength Training Specific to Running

Getting Started

As a professional running coach, I firmly believe that to improve as a runner, you need to run on a consistent basis. Furthermore, to become a faster runner, you need, at the appropriate times, to run fast. What I am saying here is that running is a sport that places very specific demands on the body, and to achieve maximum adaptation of its neurological, musculoskeletal, and cardiopulmonary systems, there is simply no substitute for running itself.

That said, I am also a firm believer in strength training as a key method of improving your running. A proper strength-training regimen can give your body the foundation and framework necessary to reduce your workout and race-recovery times. It can also provide the platform you need to train and race more competitively.

In essence, the main object of strength training (sometimes referred to as resistance training) is to break down a particular muscle or muscle group. Such a breakdown forces the body to regenerate itself to a higher degree of strength than has been previously experienced. (We discuss how this process occurs in more detail later in this chapter.) While it may be controversial to say that you can do strength training in a manner specifically designed to replicate running, I firmly believe that, when employed correctly, certain methods of strength training align themselves more closely than others to the biomechanics of running. Increased functional strength provides increased esteem and confidence, and confidence in our running ability plays a major part in a sport that is very psychological as well as physical.

Specific Strength Training

Specific strength training using good technique over a sustained period of time can directly help runners achieve good biomechanics.

Let's examine this more closely. A gifted runner may have been blessed with good mechanics, good posture, proper arm drive, and correct carriage position, thereby having the ability to move her body forward in a very efficient manner. Consistent training might also have provided good lower-body strength. However, running itself does not guarantee strength and stability through the core area (specifically the lower back, midback, abdominal, and abductor/adductor muscles—basically the inner and outer thigh and hip muscles). In the latter stages of a long run or intense workout or race, any weakness in the core area will compromise muscle integrity, and gifted mechanics will give way to poor posture and a breakdown in form. This will increase the potential for injury and in a race context might mean the difference between victory and defeat.

This problem is not limited to the core area. We have already discussed the importance of the arm drive. Mechanically, nothing positive happens until that arm is driven back, providing the counterforce to certain reactions that then result in forward locomotion. If the arm drive becomes impaired, the flight time is compromised, and again, things ultimately fall apart. Strengthening the shoulder girdle (shoulders, chest, neck, and upper-back muscles) along with the arms can prevent this premature fatigue, once again providing the potential for optimal biomechanics over a sustained period of time.

These days it is easy to find books on strength training that will prepare you for a multitude of sports. Additionally, there are activities such as Pilates, a method of training that has been around for almost a century, and various styles of yoga, a method of strength training and meditation that has been around much longer than that. These two focus on core stabilization and correct methods of breathing, both of which are integral to improved running biomechanics. Indeed, there are so many options when embarking on a new strength-training regimen that knowing where to start can be quite a daunting task. From my point of view, though, I understand that the majority of runners lead very busy lives and have a multitude of daily commitments, not the least of which is running itself. With this in mind, I have selected my top 20 strength-training exercises, each exercise specifically designed to help you increase your overall strength *as a runner.*

Do I Need to Join a Health Club?

As you have been reading this chapter, you may have been thinking that before getting your strength training under way, you would have to shell out some money and join a gym. There are a couple of good reasons why this is not the case. When you start out in a gym, it is easy to find yourself feeling overwhelmed and intimidated by the wide range and apparent complexity of strength-training apparatus. Some of the machines give the impression that you need a license to operate them. Even with several years' experience working in and around a health club setting, I can still be confused by the machinery. Sometimes I find myself looking at a machine and thinking, *It looks good, but what on earth is it for?* Or more accurately, *Which muscle group does it train?* Well, there is no need to be intimidated—I can tell you from experience that while some of this equipment is very good, much of it is superfluous.

Moving on to the second reason why it may not be necessary for you to join a gym: as with any good workout program, your strength-training schedule has to fit into your regular schedule. It may well be that you simply do not have the time to come home from work, get changed, look at that comfy couch, resist it, return an e-mail or phone call or two, get back in the car and drive to the club, find somewhere to park, check in, go to the locker room to take off your sweats, and finally get into the gym. And if you have kids—well, you can pretty much forget it! Of course, I am not suggesting that this is the case for everyone: I am just making light of a point that for many of you may have hit close to home—it can be quite a hassle to go through this kind of drill on a regular basis. Nor am I implying that you should not join a health club; far from it. Health clubs offer a valuable service. If you have the time, or make the time, to get to the health club before or after work or on the weekends or both, then that is terrific. I just know from firsthand experience that for large sections of the population, this just is not a realistic option.

While we're on the subject, I've heard just about all of the alternatives out there for the busy athlete. Most of them are also completely unrealistic. Yes, I know you can probably squeeze in 300 seated crunches in your car while driving to work and back, but is this really practical and is it really safe? Yes, you can probably drop down to the floor at the office in between phone calls and do 10 push-ups, but again, I ask you, how long will you keep that up? A day?

In summary, the following strength-training information is equally applicable regardless of your experience in strength training and whether you prefer to train in a health club setting or in the privacy of your own home.

Recommended Equipment

Before we get started, let's look at some of the equipment you may decide to use as an aid to your strength training. The following pieces of equipment should all be easy to find at good retail sporting goods stores.

Medicine Ball

The medicine ball is an extremely versatile and space-efficient piece of equipment, one that is useful for many different exercises. For example, it can be used to add resistance when doing squats and to provide an unstable platform for the experienced athlete when doing push-ups. These push-ups are performed with the hands on the ball, forcing the core area to stabilize the body during both the lifting and lowering phases. The medicine ball can also be used to add resistance to crunches.

Medicine balls come in varying weights and sizes and range in price from around $15 to $50 depending on the weight. Weights generally range from 2 pounds up to about 15 pounds.

Coach GP's recommendation: Purchase a 4-pound to 6-pound ball (novice) or 8-pound to 12-pound ball (experienced).

Stability (or Exercise) Ball

Stability balls have become very popular in recent years. They can be found in health clubs, rehabilitation centers, personal training studios, high schools, colleges, and even in offices and homes. They are relatively inexpensive, and they provide a supportive, safe, but intentionally unstable base, forcing you to challenge and strengthen your coordination, balance, and stability by working all of your smaller muscles as well as your larger, stronger muscles. If you are unfamiliar with this particular type of ball, it resembles a good old-fashioned beach ball. Some examples of possible on-the-ball exercises include push-ups, dips, hip raises, crunches, seated shoulder press, chest press, lat pullover, and hamstring curls.

Approximate cost is $15 to $30. Benefits: They challenge stability and balance, and they are space efficient and very mobile as they can be deflated and inflated as required.

Coach GP's recommendation: If you are 5 feet, 8 inches or shorter, then purchase a ball that is 45-55 centimeters. If you are taller than 5 feet, 8 inches, then buy a ball that is 65-75 centimeters.

Dumbbells

Dumbbells are space efficient, cost effective, and versatile, and they can be used for many upper-body exercises. They allow for unilateral exercise, meaning they allow you to work one side of your body at a time, preventing the dominant side from performing most of the work.

Most retailers sell dumbbells by the pound. They are now available with protective coatings to make them more user friendly and less destructive to have in your home.

Although you can spend a great deal less by purchasing piecemeal, you can buy an all-inclusive set for less than $200.

Coach GP's recommendation: In most cases for runners, weights from 5 pounds up to 50 pounds are all you need.

Resistance Bands

In essence, resistance bands are rubberized bands that provide uniform resistance in both their contraction phase and their expansion phase. Also known as resistance tubes, they have been used by therapists and sports medicine doctors for over 20 years and are now very much a part of the home and health club workout. Extremely versatile and space efficient, they can be used for both lower- and upper-body exercises. They are excellent for rehabilitation work such as rotator cuff or hip strengthening.

Resistance bands typically cost $10 or less depending on their length.

Workout Bench

A workout bench is a helpful aid for home use, enabling you to perform a variety of exercises. The benches are generally priced at $50 to $200.

Stretching Rope

Various stretching methods are available to the athlete, including static stretching and PNF (proprioceptive neuromuscular facilitation), to name but two. My preferred method of stretching is active isolated (A.I.) stretching. I believe it is both the most gentle and the most effective method of promoting increased range of motion and flexibility. It also serves as a great warm-up for the muscles.

A.I. stretching works on a two-second stretching principle whereby you actively contract the opposing muscle to the target muscle that you are stretching. For example, if you want to stretch your hamstring muscles, you need to actively contract your quadriceps muscles. The technique is easy to learn, and the only equipment recommended is an 8-foot rope or cord for self-assistance.

Two of the foremost authorities on this type of stretching are the father and son team of Jim and Phil Wharton. They are the authors of several books including *The Whartons' Stretch Book*, which is simply excellent, a must have in every runner's library. It is the most complete and most relevant stretch book of its kind, and I have recommended it to many of my athletes with great success. *The Whartons' Stretch Book* is available at *www.whartonperformance.com.*

Alternatives in a Pinch!

For the budget-conscious athlete, or if you don't happen to have your equipment handy, dumbbells can be replaced with either soup cans or telephone books. You could use either item for many of the exercises that follow in chapters 6 through 8.

Strength-Training Language

Now let's go over some terms that crop up in and around the weight room.

Reps

Repetitions of an exercise within a set.

> *Example:* A single contraction and release of a muscle or group of muscles against a specific resistance = 1 repetition.

Sets

A number of repetitions of a particular exercise.

> Example: 10 repetitions = 1 set.

Muscular Endurance

The ability of muscles to sustain work over time.

Muscular Strength

Maximal amount of force delivered or produced via a single muscular contraction.

Adaptive Training

Adaptive training takes advantage of one of the basic scientific principles of exercise—the fact that muscles subjected to stress will adapt to a level at which they can handle that stress. In other words, when training is performed properly, there is stress to the muscle groups. During recovery, an adaptive process known as the training effect occurs as a result of this stress. To keep this training effect going, there must be progression. To maintain this progression when strength training, you must first start out using an appropriate weight for a particular exercise. Then, over a series of workouts, you must increase the number of repetitions you perform.

At a point when you can comfortably achieve 12 to 15 repetitions, you can probably move up to the next level of weight, but don't forget to return to a lower starting number of repetitions for that exercise.

Warm-Up

I'm sure you would not consider running a hard track workout without having jogged several warm-up laps beforehand. Preparation for your strength training is of equal importance.

The warm-up serves to raise the core body temperature to adequate levels, increase the suppleness in the muscles and soft tissue, prepare your central nervous system, and heighten your psychological awareness and your proprioception.[1]

There is no need for anything complex; just five to 10 minutes of gentle cardiovascular exercise such as bike riding or jogging will suffice. Just remember that prior to any workout, it is critical to bring your body into a physiological state that sufficiently prepares it for the task at hand.

Breathing and Control

Be sure to utilize good breathing when strength training, ideally exhaling whenever you lift against gravity. Most important: just breathe; do not hold your breath. Use slow, controlled movements.

Caution

Finally, be sure to use your common sense. If you suffer from any serious medical problems, such as heart disease, diabetes, or high blood pressure, or if you are over 40, please see your doctor before beginning any strength-training regimen.

Top 20 Exercises

In chapters 6 through 8, I will be taking you through my top 20 exercises. These exercises will help all runners train in a safe, effective, and time-efficient manner. They require little or no investment in equipment, and most can be safely performed at home.

Strength training should cover all the major muscle groups: chest, shoulders, back, arms, abdominal muscles, and legs. My strength-training exercises are separated into the following three groups:

---

[1] The unconscious perception of movement and spatial orientation arising from stimuli within the body itself.

1. Core Stabilization
2. Upper Body
3. Lower Body

One important note from the perspective of running biomechanics is that while I strongly advocate a regular active isolated stretching regimen be included in your training (as previously mentioned), it is not essential for the runner to have ballerina-like soft-tissue flexibility. It is, however, extremely important to have excellent range of motion within the articulated joints, specifically, the ankles, knees, hips, and shoulders.

For the exercises outlined in the next three chapters, I will note which exercises are safe for all levels immediately and which should be attempted only after 30 or 90 days by newcomers to strength training.

CHAPTER 6

Strength-Training Exercises for Core Stabilization

Core Stabilization

What does core stabilization mean? If you look at an anatomical muscle chart that shows a cross-section of the major muscle groups in the human body, you may notice that all roads lead to central. That is my way of saying that all of the major muscle groups—that is, the upper-leg, back, gluteus, and abdominal muscles—lead to the body's center of gravity. This provides a central region for strength and stability.

My definition of core stability is "the ability of our muscular/neural system to give maximum support to our skeletal system in its fight against gravity."

One of the key elements to strengthening our core is strengthening the muscles that follow the channel of the spine (those are the spinal erectors and mid-upper-back muscles).

Take for example the hammer and discus throwers, whom we might be lucky enough to witness during the Olympic Games. Think about watching these athletes enter the throwing area, their set-up position, and specifically, the way they coil their bodies prior to beginning their throws. It is in these coils that the athletes' muscular forces are first harnessed and then swiftly released, producing spectacularly explosive results.

In effect, what these athletes are doing is creating a separation between their shoulders and hips, an east-west, north-south relationship between the body's upper and lower joints.

Try standing up and facing a mirror with your hips and shoulders parallel to each other. Next, while your hips remain still, slowly rotate your shoulders in a clockwise direction until they are perpendicular (or 90 degrees) to your hips. You have now created a shoulder-hip separation, which happens to be a very powerful way to create torsion in your spinal muscles. When uncoiled with velocity, this torsion can generate tremendous force.

The following core-stabilization exercises incorporate this principle of shoulder/hip separation in order to create torsional power and increase your body's core strength. Consider this: running requires torso rotation with every stride. If, as you can clearly see by watching many runners, this torso rotation is left unmanaged, your running direction will remain rudderless and weak. You will also succumb to fatigue much sooner than necessary. On the other hand, if you improve your ability to control and manage your torsional rotation, you will improve your body's ability to withstand the impact forces of running and provide a stronger platform from which to generate greater flight time. Flight time, as I'm sure you remember, is the second of the two key components essential to proper running biomechanics.

During all core exercises, you should concentrate on lengthening your body and remaining tall relative to your own height. When strength training in either a seated or a standing position, always keep yourself in extension, that is to say, with chest up, shoulders back (not rounded forward), and with a slight anterior (forward) rotation to your pelvis. This will help you remain in a strong stable position and protect your lower back.

If you have never attempted strength training, or if you have any preexisting back or other conditions, please consult with your physician before undertaking these exercises.

Core-Stabilizing Exercises

Before we begin: I note the appropriateness of each exercise for different levels of athletes. If an exercise is listed as being for all levels, it means that it can be performed by all athletes from the beginning of their program. If I note 30 or 90 days, it means that a novice athlete should wait that number of days before performing that exercise.

Level: Basic, all levels

Purpose: To strengthen the hip flexors, oblique abdominal muscles, and spinal erectors.

How to perform: Sit in an upright position, with your legs out in front of the body, and position your legs in a *V* formation. Lean back slightly and contract the abdominal muscles. Take a medicine ball and extend the arms so the ball is held out in front of the body. Your head is level, facing forward (see figure 6.1a).

a

FIGURE 6.1: (a) The proper starting position for the Russian Twist. Note the strong arch in the back and the position of the ball in relation to the torso.

Beginning with the ball out in front of the face, rotate the arms down to hip level on one side. Next, rotate the arms back to the starting position. Repeat the whole movement to the other side. (See figure 6.1 b and c.) Be sure to keep the hips facing forward throughout. As you turn, the shoulders will rotate; their finishing position will be at 90 degrees to the hips. The outside arm will remain fairly straight through the movement, and the inside arm will bend as it turns.

FIGURE 6.1: *(continued)* (b) Maintain a 90-degree separation of the shoulders to the hips and keep the head in proper alignment. (c) Position the ball perfectly in relation to the hips at the bottom of the movement.

Level: Basic, all levels

Purpose: To improve range of motion in the hip and shoulder joints.

How to perform: Lie supine (on the back), with your arms extended straight overhead. Keep the pelvis neutral and the back flat. (See figure 6.2a.)

Bring one straight arm/hand over the chest to meet its opposing leg/foot, and then lower both arm and leg to the ground (see figure 6.2b). Maintain control throughout each movement. Maintain the integrity of your back on the floor. Repeat the exercise with the other arm and leg.

FIGURE 6.2: (a) The starting position for the Single Leg V Ups. (b) Maintain a flat back and extend and stretch the arm toward the opposite leg.

Level: Advanced, 90 days

Purpose: To strengthen the abdomen, hips, lower back, and shoulders and improve range of motion in the hip and shoulder joints.

How to perform: Lie supine, with your arms extended straight overhead. Keep the pelvis neutral, the back flat, and the abdominals contracted. Raise both arms and feet four to six inches off the ground—this is the starting position (see figure 6.3a).

Bring one straight arm/hand over the chest to meet its opposing leg/foot, and then lower both arm and leg to the starting position (see figure 6.3b). Contract the abdominals. Breathe evenly. Do not allow the arms, hands, legs, or feet to touch the ground at any time. Maintain control throughout each movement. Maintain the integrity of the back on the floor. Repeat the exercise with the other arm and leg.

FIGURE 6.3: (a) The starting position for the Single Leg V Ups—Advanced. (b) To ensure the integrity of the abdominal contraction, don't let the back of your shoulders fully release onto the ground.

Level: Advanced, 90 days

Purpose: To strengthen the abdominal, hip, lower-back, and shoulder muscles and improve range of motion in the hip and shoulder joints.

How to perform: Assume the same starting position as for the previous exercise (see figure 6.4a). Simultaneously raise both the legs and the arms, moving each toward the other in a crunch. The arms/hands are trying to touch the toes (see figure 6.4b). The feet remain off the ground throughout the movement.

Slowly return to the starting position without fully releasing the shoulder blades to the floor. This ensures that the abdominal muscles remain contracted throughout the entire set. As with the two previous exercises, be sure to maintain control throughout each movement.

FIGURE 6.4: (a) The starting position of the Double Leg V Ups. (b) In mid-exercise, the legs/feet are at the proper height. The lower back must remain in contact with the ground at all times.

Level: Basic, all levels

Purpose: To strengthen the hips and improve range of motion in the hip joints.

How to perform: Lie supine, with the back flat and the arms extended out to the sides. The arms should be in line with the shoulders, palms down (see figure 6.5a).

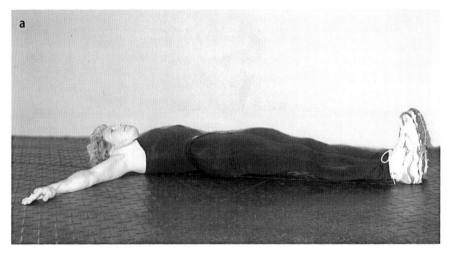

FIGURE 6.5: (a) The starting position for Eagles.

Lift and move one leg at a time in a slow, controlled swing across the body (see figure 6.5b). Touch the foot down on the ground, positioned at right angles to the torso. (See figure 6.5c.) Now return the leg back to the starting position. Repeat to the other side.

While performing this exercise, keep the back of the shoulders and arms pressed into the ground, maintaining a stretch in the shoulder joints. Begin with a modest foot placement, and then as you warm up, try to walk the foot up toward the hands. Notice that at the point where the foot touches down, you will once again have created a shoulder/hip separation.

FIGURE 6.5: *(continued)* (b) The midpoint of the movement on the way up. The right shoulder and arm stay on the ground as the right leg swings through the movement with a low sweep, not a high leg kick. (c) The finish point of the movement. The right leg is beyond 90 degrees to the left leg, which remains straight out from the hips.

REVERSE EAGLES

Level: Basic, all levels

Purpose: To strengthen the hip extensors and low back and to improve range of motion in the hip joints.

How to perform: Lie prone (facedown), arms extended out to sides, at right angles to your torso. Arms should be in line with your shoulders, palms down. Head is facing down (see figure 6.6a).

Bending at the knee, swing one leg over and across the body, creating a stretch in the hip flexor. Touch the toe to the ground (see figure 6.6b). Return your leg to the starting position and repeat on the other side. Once again this will create shoulder/hip separation. Note: As you work through this exercise, it is not necessary to try to reach the hands with the toes.

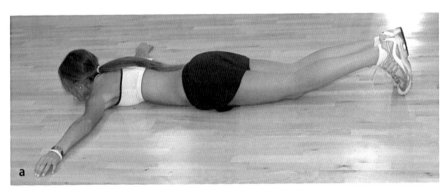

FIGURE 6.6: (a) The starting position for Reverse Eagles. (b) At the midpoint of the movement, the head remains straight, the arms are at, or close to, 90 degrees, the top leg bends at the knee, and the toe touches down. The goal is to extend the stretch out the front of the right hip. The left leg remains straight out from the hip and the separation between the shoulder and hip should be 90 degrees.

BACK EXTENSIONS WITH DIPS TO THE SIDE

Level: Basic, 30 days

Purpose: To strengthen the abdominal and oblique, low-back, midback, gluteus, and shoulder muscles. To improve the range of motion in the back and shoulder joints.

How to perform: Lie prone, with your hands placed behind the head. Your hips, legs, and feet remain on the ground. (If you are performing this exercise on a stability ball, the starting position is your torso curled around the ball. See figure 6.7a. Contract your gluteus muscles for support.

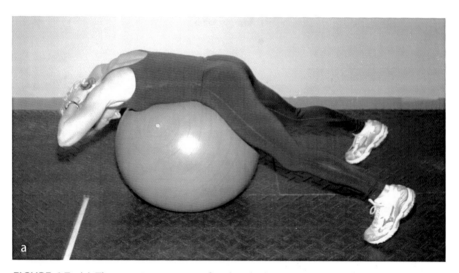

FIGURE 6.7: (a) The starting position for the Back Extensions With Dips to the Side. Note the position of the elbows, retracted shoulder blades, flat back, and wide stance for the feet.

Now lift up/extend through your mid-upper back, raising your torso off the ground (or stability ball as shown here) to a comfortable degree (see figure 6.7b). Next, while in the up position, rotate or dip one elbow down toward the ground (see figure 6.7c). Be sure to contract the gluteus muscles before raising the torso—this provides important strength and assistance to the muscles of the mid- and upper back. Also maintain a contraction of your shoulder blades through the entire set—in effect stretching out your chest.

After the dip, return to the up position, lower to the starting position, and then rise back up again and rotate/dip the other elbow to the ground. Return to the up position and lower your torso to the starting position.

FIGURE 6.7: *(continued)* (b) The extension of the back, with a wide stance of the feet and good retraction of the shoulder blades with elbows behind the head. (c) The elbows point, as if "dipping a wing."

Use good breathing; raise and lower with control. The neck should be in alignment with the spinal cord at all times. Repeat the sequence.

This exercise will most likely require some practice before you find a comfortable breathing pattern.

CRUNCHES

Level: Basic, all levels

Purpose: To strengthen the superior region of the abdominals.

How to perform: Lie supine with your knees bent and your feet planted on the floor. Place your hands behind the head. Your shoulder blades should be contracted (chest stretched). Support the head. Keep the head and neck in alignment with the spine at all times. Contract the abdominal muscles by crunching up several inches, no more. Exhale while lowering back to the starting position. Return to start position. Repeat. (See figure 6.8.)

FIGURE 6.8: The starting position for the basic Crunch.

A very effective method of increasing the challenge and maximizing the benefit of crunches is to use an unstable platform such as a stabilization ball. Doing so requires all the abdominal, lower-back, and hip muscles to assist in the work.

Level: Basic, all levels

Purpose: To strengthen the superior region of the abdominals.

How to perform: Lie supine over the ball so that the ball provides plenty of support for your low back and torso (see figure 6.9). The feet should be planted on the floor. Place the hands behind the head with shoulder blades contracted (chest stretched). Support the head. Keep the head and neck in alignment with the spine at all times. Contract the abdominal muscles by crunching up several inches, no more. Exhale while lowering the back to the starting position. For a more advanced exercise, lift one leg off the floor. Hold the (straight) leg out in front of the body. Find a stable position on the ball, and then perform the crunch as before. Maintain the contraction in the abdominal cavity throughout the entire movement.

FIGURE 6.9: The starting position for the alternate Crunches on the Ball.

Level: Basic, all levels

Purpose: To strengthen the oblique region of the abdominals.

How to perform: This exercise is basically the same as the previous one, but this time the shoulders and elbows are rotated during the crunch phase. This rotation creates a more precise contraction of the oblique abdominal muscles (the abs located at the side of the lower torso). See figure 6.10. These muscles are largely responsible for maintaining the integrity of the core region. During the lowering phase, the shoulders and elbows are rotated back to the starting position. Alternate sides through each set.

FIGURE 6.10: For Oblique Crunches, keep the elbows back to isolate the movement and the contraction of the oblique muscles. Keep the chin neutral and not pressed against your chest, which will help you maintain a fluid breathing rhythm.

Level: Basic, all levels

Purpose: To strengthen the lower region of the abdominals.

How to perform: Lie supine on the ground. Lift the knees directly over the hips. The lower legs remain parallel to the floor, making a 90-degree angle to the upper legs (see figure 6.11a).

FIGURE 6.11:
(a) In this riser version of the exercise, the hands are placed alongside the head gripping the riser. The knees are directly over the hips, the legs close together, and the back flat on the riser.

Place the hands by the sides (advanced) or under the tailbone (novice). This exercise can also be performed on a bench, in which case the hands should be overhead and gripping the top edge of the bench (good for all levels).

Using as little support as possible from the hands, pull the knees backward in the direction of the head. Keep inching back until you feel a good contraction of the lower (inferior) region of the abdominal muscles. See figure 6.11b. This will require only a small movement.

For the lowering phase, inhale, and slowly return the legs to the point where your knees are directly over the hips (see figure 6.11c). Use control. Do not let the full weight of the hips and pelvis touch the floor. The correct way to perform this exercise is to begin the next repetition before reaching the point at which all the tension is released from the abdominal cavity.

REVERSE CRUNCHES *continued*

FIGURE 6.11:
(continued) (b) In mid-movement, use your hands for support. The knees come up over the chest (no higher), and only the tailbone comes off the riser. (c) Lower slowly and with control to the starting point. The range of motion is quite small in this exercise.

CHAPTER 7

Strength-Training Exercises for the Upper Body

As you work your way through the following upper-body exercises, try to concentrate on maintaining good biomechanics and excellent posture. Be aware of the position of the body in relation to its surroundings. Maintain good head position and good, fluid breathing throughout each exercise. Make sure you keep your back in the correct position at all times. This is especially important when an exercise requires that you keep the back flat against a bench or exercise ball. When you work at the freestyle exercises (those that don't require the use of a machine or bench), be sure to keep the shoulder blades retracted in what is known as extension. This will prevent the shoulders from rounding and, more important, will ensure that the body remains in a strong, stable position throughout each exercise.

Level: Basic, all levels

Purpose: To strengthen the back, chest, shoulders, and arms.

How to perform: Place your hands on the pull-up bar, palms up (see figure 7.1a). Raise your torso until your chin is level with the bar. Engage your lower-back muscles and exhale as you lift (see figure 7.1b). Lower your torso with control.

FIGURE 7.1: (a) The starting position for Pull-Ups, with a wide-palms-up grip. This exercise can also be performed with a palms-down grip. (b) At the top of the movement, the latissimus dorsi muscles are engaged (the wings on the side of the back), the head is neutral, the body straight, and the chin to the bar.

PULL-UPS *continued*

This is an extremely hard exercise for most people, but it is a very effective method of strengthening the body to an extent where it can efficiently handle the dynamic movement of its own weight. Pull-ups are performed almost exclusively in a gym setting; however, it is possible to purchase and install a horizontal pull-up bar. If you do install the bar, please be certain that it is both secure and strong enough to support several times your body weight.

If you are already familiar with this exercise, I recommend that you complete two sets at close to maximum effort, allowing for adequate but minimum recovery between sets and utilizing two different hand grips. The first grip we've already explained.

• *Second grip:* Known as a chin-up. Use a narrower grip, palms facing in (see figure 7.2a). Raise your torso until your chin is level with the bar. Engage the back muscles and exhale as you lift (see figure 7.2b). Lower with control.

The combination of the two different grips will maximize the benefit to the arms, chest, and back muscles. Make sure to lower with control and always complete the full range of motion.

• *Note for novices:* Your goal should be to complete one pull-up. If you find this is not yet possible, begin by performing a negative pull-up. Stand on a box that allows you to reach and hold on to the pull-up bar at apex of a regular pull-up. Use a narrow-grip, chin-up style. Step off the box. Maintain the position for a second at the apex of the pull-up. Then inhale and lower the body with control; keep lowering until the feet touch the ground. (If necessary, perform this negative pull-up with the assistance of a partner. The partner should provide support by holding on to your hips.)

Step back up on the box and repeat five to six times if possible. Over the course of 30 days, if performed two to three times per week, you should develop sufficient strength to attempt a full pull-up. If you are still unable to complete one after 30 days, continue with negative pull-ups by increasing the repetitions each week, periodically challenging yourself to do a regular pull-up. Persist, and you will succeed. Always make sure to breathe through the entire movement.

PULL-UPS *continued*

FIGURE 7.2: (a) The starting position for the chin-up style of Pull-Up. This is a slightly easier exercise to perform. The hands are closer together, and palms are facing each other, allowing the biceps muscles to provide greater assistance during the movement. (b) At the top of the movement, the body is straight, the chin to the bar, and the feet together.

Level: All, except beginner

Purpose: To strengthen the chest, back, arms, shoulders, and core.

How to perform: Keep the torso straight, hands shoulder width apart, abdominal muscles contracted (see figure 7.3a). During the lowering phase, the arms are hinged at the elbow. The elbows remain close to the torso and do not stray outward. Lower with control (see figure 7.3b). The upper arm should finish at 90 degrees to the lower arm. The torso and head should finish just above the ground. Exhale as you lift.

FIGURE 7.3: (a) The starting position for the Push-Up on the ball alternate. Note the straight alignment of the body and shoulders directly over the wrists. (b) During the lowering phase, keep the body straight, the elbows in and alongside the torso, and the feet together.

ADVANCED PUSH-UPS—FEET ON EXERCISE OR BEACH BALL

How to perform: An innovative, more advanced way to do push-ups is for the athlete to place the feet on a large stability (or beach-type) ball. As shown in figure 7.4 a and b, place the hands on the ground, shoulder width apart, and complete push-ups with a full range of motion (as in regular push-ups). The inclusion of this type of unstable surface forces the core muscles to work extra hard just to keep the body in a neutral starting position.

FIGURE 7.4: (a) The starting position for the advanced feet on the ball style of Push-Up. Note the straight body angle and the shoulders directly over the wrists. (b) During the lowering phase, keep the body straight, the elbows in and alongside the torso, and the feet together.

For an even harder push-up challenge, try performing them with your feet on a bench or set of risers and your hands placed close together on an exercise or beach ball (see figure 7.5 a and b). You will feel an extra intensity, particularly in your triceps and forearms.

FIGURE 7.5: (a) For this advanced Push-Up, keep the body straight and the shoulders directly over the wrists. (b) As you lower with control, the elbows remain alongside the body, and the ball remains under the head, neck, and upper chest. Keep a straight alignment the entire length of your body.

For those of you thinking about doing a push-up with your knees on the floor, don't waste your time. Here is the plan for you. Just as you perform negative pull-ups, so you can also perform negative push-ups. They will certainly take some extra effort on your part, but it will be well worth it.

BEGINNER PUSH-UPS (NO KNEES DOWN)

How to perform: Begin on all fours, the hands shoulder width apart and the feet slightly closer together. Raise the hips until only the hands and feet remain on the ground. Now for the hard part. Walk the hands forward until your body is straight and knees, hips, and shoulders are in line. Next, inhale and slowly lower the body to the floor. Focus on lowering with control. Take as much time as possible to complete the whole movement—up to five seconds if you can. Once on the floor, rest a moment or two, return to the all-fours position, and repeat the movement. Complete as many as you can, increasing the repetitions until you can comfortably complete two sets of 10. (Take a 60-second break or as long as you need to remain comfortable between each set.) Once you can complete two sets of 10 repetitions, you are ready to begin regular push-ups.

ONE-ARM ROW

Level: Basic, all levels

Purpose: To strengthen the back, arms, and shoulders.

How to perform: This exercise can be done with the help of a bench or a stability ball. Alternatively, you can simply lean the torso forward, using the front leg for support. Either way, make sure you select an appropriate weight with which to perform the exercise. If you are using a bench, place the right knee and right hand on the bench. The left leg should be straight, with the left foot placed on the ground about one shoulder width away from the body and slightly behind the hip. If using the stability ball, adopt the same leg and hand positions as shown with the stability ball example in figure 7.6. In each case the back should be flat, not rounded or hunched, and the neck should be aligned (see figure 7.6). Inhale to begin and then, on the exhale, start to lift the weight with the left arm. Raise the weight slowly, under control, and in a slight backward motion (as if you were sawing a piece of wood). Bring the weight alongside the hip and then return it to the starting position. Complete two sets of 10 to 12 repetitions, then switch sides, or alternatively complete one set per side and repeat.

If you are not using a bench or ball for support, complete the exercise in almost the same fashion, but place the right leg out in front of the body. The right leg should be slightly bent. Place the right hand on the thigh, just above the knee (not on the kneecap), and lean forward. Be sure to maintain a straight back alignment. Complete the exercise as described above.

ONE-ARM ROW *continued*

FIGURE 7.6: A One-Arm Row executed on the ball. Note the strong "stride out" leg placement and flat back. Draw the weight into the hip, not up to the shoulder.

INCLINE CHEST PRESS

Level: Basic, all levels

Purpose: To strengthen the shoulders, chest, and arms.

How to perform: This exercise is my secret weapon! Set up an incline bench at about a 45-degree angle and select your weights. This exercise relies almost exclusively on a small muscle group in the shoulders with the dumbbells being held away from the body. For these two reasons, you will find that you are better off beginning with a fairly light weight.

Sit on an incline bench, set at 45 degrees, with the lumbar spine (lower-back area) pressed firmly into the seat back. Hold a dumbbell in each hand, and bring the hands up to shoulder level. The upper and lower arms should form a 90-degree angle. Keep the hands out wide, just outside the line of the shoulder. To help determine whether you are in the correct position, trace an imaginary line from hand to hand across your chest. The arms should be in football goalpost position.

Now—with authority—press the dumbbells away from the body until your arms are out straight, maintaining shoulder-width distance between your hands. Exhale as you lift. The key is to press outward more than up-ward (as in a standard incline chest press) emphasizing shoulder recruit-ment. Return to the starting position. Repeat 10 to 12 times, completing one to two sets. Do not increase the weight until you can complete two sets comfortably. It is very important to keep your lower back pressed into the bench and your abdominal muscles contracted throughout the entire movement and to exhale as you press out.

Also note that depending on your neck design, you might feel more comfortable with your head pressed back into the top of the incline bench, or you might feel better with the head lifted slightly away from the bench. I have tried both positions, and providing you are using the appropriate weight, either is fine.

- *Adaptation for the exercise ball.* Begin by lying back on the ball with the feet placed in front of you. Your feet should be wide enough apart to provide a stable platform. Slide the body down the ball toward the floor so that the ball fits snugly against your back and shoulders. The torso should be leaning back against the ball in an incline position. See figure 7.7a. (Note: Place your weights on the floor close to the ball before you begin so that they are easy to pick up once you are in position.) Complete the exercise as described for the incline bench (see figure 7.7b).

INCLINE CHEST PRESS *continued*

This exercise develops both front and outside shoulder strength—strength upon which you'll be able to rely whether you are using it in a final kick against the clock or against an opponent in an upcoming race!

FIGURE 7.7: (a) The starting position for the Incline Chess Press. (b) As you press the dumbbells upward, maintain shoulder-width distance between your hands, and exhale as you lift.

Level: Basic, all levels

Purpose: To strengthen the chest, back, midback, arms, and shoulders and range of motion in the shoulder joint.

How to perform: Lie back on a stability ball, placing the feet shoulder width apart and flat on the floor. Hold the weight over your chest (see figure 7.8a). It is extremely important that the hips be pressed upward while the abdominal muscles are contracted—maintaining the integrity and strength of the body from the knees through to the shoulders. Both neck and head must be supported by the ball and remain in alignment with the rest of the body.

Inhale, and lower the weight behind your head (see figure 7.8b). Return to the starting position, exhaling as you lift.

• *Adaptation for the bench.* Lie back on the bench. Your feet should be either on the end of the bench, with legs bent and feet flat (see figure 7.9a), or straddling the bench so the feet are on the floor. It is imperative that the lumbar spine remain firmly pressed against the bench.

Now that you are set, take a single dumbbell and hold it in a vertical position by cupping the hands under and around the weight's top end (see figure 7.9a). The weight should hang straight down, perpendicular to the ground. The weight should both start and finish in a position directly over the sternum (breastbone). Take the hands back over the head, keeping the arms straight. When you reach the point at which the shoulders will not travel any farther, bend slightly at the elbow to squeeze out a little extra range of motion (see figure 7.9b). Do not force the issue—as your body becomes more familiar with the exercise, the range of motion will slightly increase. This in turn will help the arm's range of motion when you are running. Finally, straighten the arms so that the forearms align with the upper arms, then return the straightened arms to the starting position over the sternum.

Inhale deeply during the lowering phase; this will help to expand the chest cavity. Exhale as you lift. (When it comes to running, practicing deep breathing is an excellent exercise in its own right.)

LAT PULLOVER *continued*

FIGURE 7.8: (a) The starting position for the Lat Pullover on an exercise ball. Note the straight body position—hips pressed up (i.e., no sag in the back), ankles under the knees, the hands inverted and cupped around the dumbbell head. The ball supports the torso. (b) As you lower the weight behind you, maintain the integrity of the alignment and move through a comfortable range of motion.

LAT PULLOVER *continued*

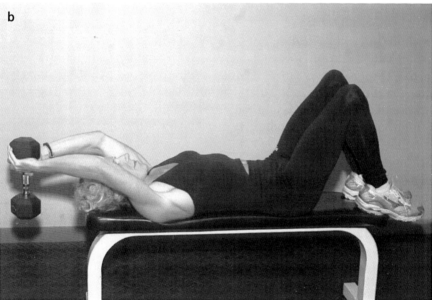

FIGURE 7.9: (a) The Lat Pullover on a bench. The back is flat, the knees bent, the feet together, and the knees over the ankles. (b) With the hands inverted and the dumbbell head cupped in your hands, lower the weight through a comfortable range of motion behind the head and return to the starting position.

Level: Basic, all levels

Purpose: To strengthen the chest, back, arms, and shoulders.

How to perform: If you are strength-training in a gym, then take advantage of the dip bar for this exercise (ask the personal trainer on duty to point it out if necessary).

For athletes new to strength training: Sit on the edge of a bench or exercise ball. Place the hands next to the hips. Your fingers should either be curled over the edge of the bench or resting on top of the ball, facing forward. Feet should be in a firm shoulder-width stance.

Slide the buttocks just off the edge of the bench or ball. See figure 7.10a. Bend the arms and lower the torso until the angle between the upper and lower arms is approaching 90 degrees, a point where the shoulder is just above the height of the elbow (not below). See figure 7.10b. Return to the starting position, and exhale as you lift. The head should be kept level and the shoulder blades kept retracted throughout. This will ensure that you are in extension and not rounded in the back.

• *For the advanced athlete*: Stand on the dip-bar supports and place each hand on the parallel bars by your sides, palms down. Step off the leg supports and either bend your lower legs up behind you at a 90-degree angle to the upper legs, or cross them over (see figure 7.11a). While maintaining complete control of the body (not letting it swing), bend the arms and lower slowly to a position where the upper arm and shoulder are slightly higher than your elbow (not lower!) (see figure 7.11b). Return to the starting position by driving upward using the strength of the arms; the arms should reach an extended or straightened position. Do not touch the feet down until the last repetition is complete.

• *If you are completely new to this exercise:* If you are just starting out, then try to complete just one repetition at a time with a short recovery in between. Be consistent with this exercise until you can build up to two sets of 25 repetitions. Once you've met this goal, it's time to graduate to the dip bar. Begin with fewer repetitions and work your way up from there. If you are strength-training at home, then continue to use the bench or the ball and just keep increasing your repetitions by adding more sets.

If you happen to be using a bench, there is another method by which you can increase the degree of difficulty. Simply place your feet, with legs straight out in front of you, onto another bench or chair. The intensity of the exercise will now approach that of regular dip-bar dips.

DIPS/BENCH DIPS *continued*

FIGURE 7.10: (a) The starting position for Dips. (b) Lower your body until the angle between the upper and lower arm is approaching 90 degrees.

DIPS/BENCH DIPS *continued*

FIGURE 7.11: (a) The starting position for Dips on a dip bar. (b) Lower your body until the angle between the upper and lower arm is approaching 90 degrees. Elbows remain in, alongside the torso, chin neutral.

CHAPTER 8

Strength-Training Exercises for the Lower Body

Just as when you are strength-training the upper body, proper biomechanics and posture are essential when strengthening the lower body, in addition to your awareness of your body position in relation to its surroundings.

Proper body position during the specific movements is described with each exercise.

Strengthening the lower body is critical to increasing power in the legs and core, which directly relates to your efficiency in the drive-off and support phases of the running movements. Furthermore, the greater the strength in the legs, the greater economy achieved during required muscular contractions at specific efforts and speeds during the run. Finally, the stronger the legs, the less susceptible you will be to injury from the impact forces of running in addition to being able to recover more quickly from each training session.

The squat is a power exercise involving compound movement, meaning that it requires effort from more than one muscle group at a time. There are many ways to perform squats, but on the next five pages are the two that I find most effective.

Level: 30 days

Purpose: To strengthen the anterior tibialis (shin muscle), calves, quads, hamstrings, gluteus, lower back, and hip flexors.

How to perform: Stand with the feet shoulder width apart. There should be a slight anterior rotation to the hips. The shoulder blades should be gently squeezed together to prevent rounding in the back. If you are using a bar, place your hands outside the shoulders, palms up, and facing the bar—arms should form a football goalpost position (see figure 8.1a).

Contract the abdominal muscles and breathe in as you lower your torso. Position the body as if you were going to sit back into a chair or stool. Keep your weight toward the middle of the feet. Your knees must not extend anywhere near the toes. In fact, if this exercise is performed correctly, the knees hardly move at all. The hips should be lowered only to an angle that is greater than 90 degrees to your knees. In other words, do not drop the butt below the height of the knees. Try to be even in the delivery of power through both legs (see figure 8.1b).

- *For the advanced athlete:* Squats can be performed freestyle (without the use of a machine or other equipment). Weights can be carried either in each hand or via a weight bar placed behind the head and across the top of the shoulders.

It's a good idea to practice the movement without using any weights at first. Just sit down on a chair or stool and touch the butt down only lightly before lifting back up to the starting position. Maintain excellent posture (the shoulder blades are contracted, not rounded) through the entire movement.

You will notice that the angle between your torso and upper leg at the bottom of the movement is very similar to the angle between the upper and lower leg.

- *For the novice athlete:* This method is recommended not only for novices but also for anyone who has had a history of knee problems or who is in rehab. (It works perfectly well for advanced athletes too.) It involves the use of an exercise ball.

Place the ball behind the small of the back. Lean against a firm, flat wall with the ball between your back and the wall (see figure 8.2a). Adopt the same starting position as described in the first squats method. Note, however, that since the ball is now there for support, it's possible to

SQUATS *continued*

a b

FIGURE 8.1: (a) The starting position of the Squat. Make sure your feet are shoulder width apart and the weight is over the middle of your feet. (b) At the outset of the movement, bend at the hips as if sitting into a chair. Do not slide the knees forward. Maintain an arch in your back (i.e., not rounded).

be more flexible with the placement of the feet. The knees must still be protected by keeping them from extending out beyond the toes. Lower the body down to the same squat position as described in the advanced method above (see figure 8.2b). Exhale as you straighten.

SQUATS *continued*

a

FIGURE 8.2: (a) The starting position of the Squat performed with a ball behind the back. (b) As you lower your body, the ball provides added support and allows you to place your feet farther out in front, which will minimize stress on the knees.

b

Level: Basic, all levels

Purpose: To strengthen the calves, anterior tibialis (shin muscles), quads, hamstrings, gluteus, and hip flexors. Most of us have one side of our body that is stronger than the other. This exercise is designed to address that imbalance as you strengthen one leg at a time.

How to perform: Begin in a standing position. Keep the back in extension. Place a weight in each hand or a light bar across the shoulders behind the head. Take a step forward (like a running stride) with one leg (see figure 8.3a). Lower the back knee to floor and keep your front knee over the heel. When you bring your center of gravity directly downward, the front leg will bend around the knee joint (see figure 8.3b).

FIGURE 8.3: (a) The starting position for the Split Squats/Static Lunge. The shoulders are over the hips and the front foot is out in front of the back foot, much like the running stride position.

SPLIT SQUATS OR STATIC LUNGE *continued*

FIGURE 8.3:
(continued) (b) At the bottom of the movement, the back knee is directly under the hip and stops just before making contact with the ground.

b

It is imperative that the front knee be kept over the ankle. Do not allow the knee to drift toward the toes. Your shoulders remain in alignment over the hips. The back leg will have some bend to it and will be resting on the ball of the back foot. At the bottom of the movement, your back knee will come very close to touching the ground. Exhale as you lift. Complete the set, switch legs, and repeat. Alternatively, switch legs upon the completion of two sets, whichever you prefer.

You will almost certainly feel intensity in the front of the back leg in the upper thigh/hip area. This is the stretching of your hip muscles. It is the front leg (specifically the quadriceps) that is providing the power required to first lower the torso and then raise it back up to the starting position.

Level: Basic, all levels

Purpose: To strengthen the quadriceps.

How to perform: Raise one leg (at a time) with control. Aim for maximal extension. Squeeze quadriceps muscle. Lower the leg with control (see figure 8.4).

FIGURE 8.4: The Leg Extension utilizing body weight only.

If performing this exercise in a gym, you can work with either a leg-extension machine or an exercise ball.

• *Using the leg-extension machine:* If you are using a leg-extension machine, it is best to work one leg at a time. Working both legs at the same time can compound the imbalance that already exists within our leg musculature since it usually causes the dominant leg to do most of the work.

Use the single-leg approach and a very light, manageable weight.

Begin with the lower leg at a 90-degree angle to the upper leg. Make sure that the toes are slightly turned out, a position that will accentuate the strengthening of the interior lower quadriceps, known as the VMO (or vastus medialis oblique). The VMO is the main stabilizer of the knee.

Straighten the lower leg up to the point where it is in line with the upper leg, creating a brief maximal contraction of the quadriceps muscles. Lower the leg slowly and with control and return to the starting position.

It is important to focus on going through a complete range of motion and a maximal contraction with a one-second hold at the top of the movement. This is because the VMO maximally contracts only during the last five degrees of extension. Through experience gained by coaching large numbers of female runners in my women's running group, the Iron Maidens of Santa Cruz, California, I can tell you that this lower interior quadriceps is a particularly vulnerable area in the female runner's makeup. By strengthening the VMO, women can go a long way toward eliminating the knee and knee-related problems encountered during their running careers.

You should complete 10 to 12 leg extensions per side and then repeat. Or again, you could switch to the second side after completing two sets.

• *Using a medicine ball:* Sit on the bench or set of risers, holding the rear edge for support. Perform a double-leg extension by placing a small medicine ball between the feet and following the previous instructions for the single-leg extension (see figure 8.5). Over time, using this method will increase the strength of the hip adductor (interior hip/thigh) stabilizing muscles. This is useful to runners as we rely on these muscles a great deal for stability during forward movement.

• *Using an exercise ball or bench:* If you are performing this exercise on an exercise ball or bench, then adding ankle weights becomes an option. Follow the directions as detailed for the leg-extension machine, making sure to sit on the ball with excellent posture.

• *Recommendation for novice runners:* I recommend that novice runners complete this exercise twice a week for a total of three weeks before adding more sets to your routine. Since this exercise can prove very effective using nothing but the leg's own weight, you should wait four to six weeks before adding any (light) weights.

LEG EXTENSION *continued*

FIGURE 8.5: The Double-Leg Extension with a medicine ball between the feet. Note the position of the arms for support in addition to proper posture.

Before we discuss hamstring curls, by way of introduction, we need to pause briefly to discuss this temperamental muscle group. The hamstrings comprise three major muscles at the back of the upper leg. Originating in the pelvic region and attaching below the knee, they play an integral role in the rotation of the leg and flexion and extension of the knee.

Hamstring injuries vary in severity from minor tears to catastrophic tears that can take months to rehabilitate. My recommended exercises will go a long way in helping you to avoid these injuries, but first let's refresh our knowledge about exactly what happens during the runner's leg cycle and why hamstring injuries are so easily sustained.

If we take a look at the leg cycle, we will see that

1. the right leg drives off;
2. the right leg then progresses through its recovery;
3. the right leg then swings through to become the lead leg;
4. there is then a point in flight when gravity begins to take over and the right leg moves into its descent and returns to the support phase.

During the forward-swing phase, the hamstring is extremely susceptible to injury. Here's why.

- In the beginning of the leg's flight phase, the lower half (from the knee to the foot) of the right leg will be angled behind the upper half.

- The upper half of the leg continues on its forward path until it reaches its hinge moment (remember, this is the point at which it can travel no more).

- The lower half of the leg will swing forward, hinged as it is at the knee, and it is this swing-through that puts the lower hamstring under extreme duress. Its whole role is to decelerate the lower leg, which would otherwise snap like a twig at the knee. There is an eccentric contraction whereby the muscles simultaneously stretch yet contract to slow the movement of the lower leg as it swings through. It is the forceful nature of this deceleration process that often causes hamstring injuries. There are three effective but slightly different methods for strengthening the hamstring muscles that I want to explain.

Level: Basic, all levels

Purpose: To strengthen the hamstrings.

How to perform: The first hamstring exercise, hamstring curls, is the most familiar. In a gym setting, lie facedown (prone) on a set of risers (see below) or a leg-curl machine. Starting with your legs straight out behind you, contract your gluteal muscles to protect the back, then raise one leg at a time in a smooth, controlled manner (see figure 8.6). Continue raising the leg, being sure to complete the full range of motion. Squeeze the hamstring at the top of the movement and then lower with control to the starting position. The nonworking leg remains on the bench. Remember to exhale as the leg is raised and inhale as the leg is lowered.

For most runners, the hamstrings will be a good deal weaker than the quadriceps. This is why I recommend selecting a very light starting weight for leg curls. Also make sure to keep your body flat and pressed into the bench. I cannot tell you how many times I have seen athletes select weights that are far too heavy. To lift the weight, their bodies launch into a whole series of involuntary compensatory movements. The buttocks rise off the bench to help the hip flexors assist in the lift by shortening up (see figure 8.7).

FIGURE 8.6: The Prone Hamstring Curl on a riser bench using body weight only. This exercise can also be performed with one leg at a time.

HAMSTRING CURLS *continued*

FIGURE 8.7: An example of bad form—the hips rising off the bench to compensate for too heavy a weight.

This is akin to standing upright and trying to bring the heel up to your buttocks while in the process of raising the heel, bending over at the waist, and bringing the knee in the direction of the chest (hip flexion). That is my analogy of what athletes are mistakenly doing when lifting too heavy a weight on the leg-curl machine.

Select a weight light enough to allow you to bring your heel toward your buttocks without flexing at the hip. You can choose to strengthen both legs together or one at a time. As per the preceding leg exercises, I recommend strengthening each leg individually.

Complete 10 to 12 leg curls per side and then repeat. As with leg extensions, novices should complete this exercise twice a week for a total of three weeks before adding more sets to your routine. Otherwise I recommend one to two sets per leg.

• *For the nongym setting #1:* This hamstring exercise works well with the assistance of an exercise ball. Lie on your back, legs straight, heels on the ball, hands by hips, and palms down (see figure 8.8a). Contract the gluteal and abdominal muscles and press up into a bridge position, rolling the ball in with both feet toward the gluteus as far as you can, using

HAMSTRING CURLS *continued*

the arms for support (see figure 8.8b). Exhale as you roll the ball in. The raised hips make a straight line between heels and shoulders. Return to the starting position.

FIGURE 8.8: (a) The starting position for the Supine Leg Curl. (b) Be sure to use the hands and arms for support and maintain a stable pelvis.

HAMSTRING CURLS *continued*

The novice athlete should begin by using both legs to perform the exercise. The advanced athlete can place one heel on the ball while holding the other leg straight out about 12 to 18 inches above the ball. The heel on the ball will be placed more centrally. This is a much, much harder exercise. You will feel this exercise intensely in the calf while the abdominal muscles will have to work hard to maintain stability. Begin with one set of 10 repetitions and build up from there.

- *For the nongym setting #2:* The final method for strengthening the hamstrings specifically parallels the running motion in terms of how the hamstring muscles are recruited. This is the kneeling hamstring exercise.

This exercise requires the assistance of a training partner. If that isn't practical for you, then you can try some other methods of anchoring your feet. Tucking the toes under the edge of the couch will often work, as long as your feet remain firmly on the floor throughout the exercise.

Begin in a kneeling position, with the lower legs at a 90-degree angle to the upper legs. The lower legs should be straight out behind the body with the soles of the feet facing up. Knees, hips, and shoulders should all be in alignment. Be sure to maintain good posture with the back remaining in extension (shoulder blades contracted) and the arms by the sides (see figure 8.9a).

Have your partner stand on the underside of your toes. Keeping your gluteus muscles (buttocks) contracted, your shoulders aligned over your hips, and your back straight, lean forward in a fixed manner, maintaining the straight alignment from knee to shoulder (somewhat resembling a downhill ski-jumper position). See figure 8.9b. Move very, very slowly and proceed only to the farthest point (a matter of inches) at which you can still return to the starting position solely by contracting the hamstrings and gluteals. Exhale as you return to the starting position. Try to make sure you contract the hamstrings with equal force on either side.

The stronger the hamstrings, the farther you will be able to go. If you begin to cramp up, just place your hands on the floor in front of you and bail out of the movement.

Novice athletes should repeat this exercise five to eight times per one set. Advanced athletes can complete two sets of 10 to 12 repetitions. You will need to demonstrate good common sense and judgment as you will be determining your own range of motion (that is, it will not be predetermined by a machine).

HAMSTRING CURLS *continued*

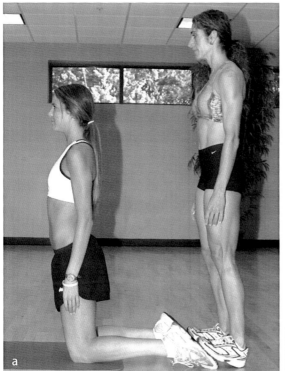

FIGURE 8.9: (a) Kneeling upright, secure your position by having a partner stand on the balls of your feet. (b) As you move forward from the knee, the shoulders should be aligned over the hips and the back straight.

a

b

Planning Your Strength-Training Program

Chapters 6, 7, and 8 have outlined my top 20 exercises for strength training specific to running. To be a better runner, you need to run, period. However, the exercises described in these three chapters have helped me and countless athletes that I have worked with improve our "chassis and drive trains." They will work for you too.

How much strength training should you do? I recommend following a three-week mesocycle as shown in the table below. (The term mesocycle will be explained in chapter 11; in essence, it means a two- to three-week training period.)

TABLE 8.1 **Three-week mesocycle**

	Week #1	Week #2	Week #3
Day #1	upper body and core strength	lower body and core strength	upper body and core strength
Day #2	lower body and core strength	upper body and core strength	lower body and core strength
Day #3	upper body and core strength	lower body and core strength	upper body and core strength

Note: During specific parts of your training cycles—the racing season, for example, or within three weeks of a marathon—you will need to adjust your strength-training regimen. There will be times—directly before and after the marathon, for example—when you won't do any strength training. As always, use good common sense when it comes to your training and remember that consistency throughout your training cycle will be the key to your success.

Conclusion

By strengthening your lower, upper, and core areas, you can increase your lean muscle mass. Since muscle cells require more energy and burn more calories than fat cells, your metabolism is increased even when you are at rest. This has the added benefit of keeping your weight at an optimal level. Furthermore, strength training increases the tenacity of our soft tissue, including cartilage, tendons, and ligaments. Strength training also increases our muscular power, endurance, stamina, and coordination and our ability to withstand the overall stresses brought on by the rigors of daily running, training, and racing.

Are these the only exercises to do? Absolutely not! There are countless routines, programs, exercise styles, and methods. I am simply providing you with my top 20 exercises that in my experience are safe, time-efficient, and adaptable to either a gym or home setting. They also target areas that are critical to your running fluidity and strength. In strength training, just as in running, it is imperative to have a plan to follow to know where you have come from, where you are, and where you are going. Incorporating these exercises into some or all of your plan will help you achieve your running goals while remaining less prone to injury.

PART III

The Rest of Your Program

CHAPTER 9

The Fire Within

Until this point in the book, I have identified and discussed the basic elements involved in increasing your efficiency and economy as a runner. In addition, you now have an effective and time-efficient strength-training program to complement your running. What follows in this chapter is the discussion of another extremely important component of a well-balanced training program: desire and motivation.

If you are embarking on a running program, know that desire from within is where it all begins. All of the knowledge gained from the previous chapters will be of use only if you are motivated to get out your door in the first place. Thousands of athletes are still waiting to get started, and just as many exercise inconsistently. How can you avoid being one of them? How can you hold on to your motivation?

A Runner Named Pre

In 1972, a 21-year-old University of Oregon runner by the name of Steve Prefontaine represented the United States at the Munich Olympics in the 5,000-meter final. He was an extremely gifted athlete and supremely confident in spite of the fact that he was more used to racing against his college peers than competing on the world's largest track and field stage against some of the finest runners in history.

It is well documented now that in a valiant effort, Pre gave it his all in his attempt for gold. He was in the lead for much of the race, but in the end he was beaten by a very seasoned group of Europeans and settled for an agonizing fourth place. This was a bitter defeat for the young man from Coos Bay, Oregon, a runner who had become accustomed to winning.

Legend has it that after Prefontaine returned to the United States, his Olympic and University of Oregon coach, Bill Bowerman, took him aside after he missed several track practices. He said something to the effect of this: "Steve, if you want to be on this team, then show up at 6:00 A.M. for practice and I will give you the workout; otherwise you will not make the team. I cannot coach the desire in you; that must come from within."

Prefontaine did show up for practice. He put his Olympic defeat behind him and went on to hold seven American records in distances ranging from 2,000 to 10,000 meters before his untimely death in May 1975 from a single-car crash. This tragedy did not come before Pre had established himself as a legend in the running world, a legend that has only grown stronger over time.

Prefontaine's story serves as an example of desire, motivation, and a bloody-minded determination to succeed. If you believe that you can be motivated by outside forces, such as a girlfriend, boyfriend, husband, wife, mother, or father, then you are mistaken. Certainly some amount of impetus can be gained from these relationships, but as far as long-term training goes, it will be short lived. The same can be said of extraneous motives to train, such as exclusively to lose weight or to look good or to fit in those old jeans.

We are constantly inundated through the electronic and print media, including obnoxious infomercials, with information on how we should look. We should be taller or thinner, have more hair, have less hair, have more sex, eat this food, take that pill—and so it goes on, in an endless carousel of confusion. The harsh reality is there are no shortcuts, no easy ways to long-term health and fitness, no wonder drug, no magic pill. Neither will you remain motivated and achieve your goals through rudderless exercising. What you need is an intelligent, well-structured training plan—a plan designed to inspire you to complete all the hard work it requires.

There are a number of different issues to be considered when discussing the topic of motivation. It is a vast and complex subheading under the umbrella of training.

In the Trenches:
Blue-Collar Ideas That Really Work

First, *the intensity of the desire must match or surpass the demand of the specific goal or goals*. Many people would truly like to experience the drama of completing a marathon or the sexiness of racing a mile, in particular to enjoy the feelings of heroism therein, in addition to basking in the applause and adulation bestowed upon the runner at the conclusion of the race from the spectators. That warrior mentality is within all of us. However, some admit the finishing experience to be appealing but equally accept that they have no stomach to negotiate the training. I doubt that the readers of this book are among this group. However, they may be among the group that wishes to experience the aforementioned drama, heroism, and adulation; is willing to take on the training but lacks the knowledge to do so; or, more commonly, fails to achieve the consistency required to complete the goal, coming up short, frustrated, and with a complete lack of satisfaction and possibly even reduced self-esteem.

Sequential, progressive training that is planned and methodical is tedious but essential. Knowing this going in is imperative, and having premeditated ideas for how to deal with the blahs and training blues is paramount if you're going to be successful on a long-term, ongoing basis.

Every contingency must be made. For example, it is great to have a training partner or training partners. They can keep you accountable on those cold winter nights when, after a hard day's work, the couch and a log fire can be significantly more appealing than plowing through your six-mile recovery run in the wind, freezing rain, and a windchill of 15 degrees. However, your training partner or partners can succumb to the same dread of the midweek, rain-soaked six-miler and the appeal of the log fire just as easily as you, so now what do you do? In addition, many runners out there are living in rural areas where they may not have access to a training partner.

I said every contingency must be made, and therefore I want you to employ the same technique that has served me so well for so many years.

The Ultimate Training Partner and Foe

What I am about to tell you is self-discovered. Never have I read it, been taught it, or had it recommended to me.

In the early years of my adult running career, after 1990, I found myself to be motivated on a long-term basis as many of you are. However, motivation is a psychological response to a given goal. For example, in 1993 I raced the Honolulu Marathon. In early January that year, on that typical cold winter's evening, would I be motivated enough to get out and do that recovery run when I still have months and months before my marathon? As daunting as the marathon distance is, would it be intimidating enough to force me out the door several months ahead of time in the freezing rain, or could I take the *mañana* approach? What is one missed session? It can wait until tomorrow, right?

Perhaps one missed session is not that big a deal. Perhaps it is. One thing is for sure: it is rarely one missed session. Once a precedent has been set, typically the trend remains and it is a dangerous trend.

I came up with a different plan. I needed not just motivation but a physiological stimulus. I needed to be inspired on a minute-by-minute, moment-by-moment, training-session-by-training-session basis.

As a professional coach, I demand that my athletes train in the fashion of an Olympian and practice the same disciplined principles that the very best at their respective crafts do each and every day—train hard and train smart and work toward becoming faster than they were the day before.

One day many years ago, I was thinking long and hard about becoming better, about becoming stronger, fitter, and faster. I was in marathon mode at the time, and one day I was thinking of the marathon world record set several years before by Ethiopian Belayneh Dinsamo in Rotterdam, Holland. I was thinking about the courage, determination, and hard work that had to gel for this amazing accomplishment to materialize. I was certain that Belayneh, in preparation for his world record race back in 1988, would not have skipped a workout because of inclement conditions. It was now the winter of 1992-1993, and bringing my mind to the present time, I wondered where Belayneh was now. Was he still running? I thought of who were his latest challengers and the type of training that they must be doing to break Belayneh's world record. And so it hit me—it is often said that the best things in life are free and that the best-laid plans are the simple ones. I was about to come up with the simplest of plans, one that would stand the test of time.

Each and every day, I would work toward the world record time in the event that I was training for. In early 1993, Belayneh's marathon world record still stood at 2:06:50, and my current marathon best at the time was 3:28.

Do not misunderstand me. I am not implying that I would break the world record, not at all. But what I am talking about is the aforementioned inspiration to train as smart and as hard as I could every day, even if it was months ahead of my goal race. Coming up with the idea that the world record holder would be somewhere on this planet training hard would provide the impetus and inspiration that would get me out that door every morning, afternoon, or night. He would become my friend, training partner, and foe. It was his world record that I was looking to close upon, and yet it was his determined methods of training that would inspire me. Remember, it is not just about the motivation; it is about the moment-by-moment, day-by-day inspiration to get you through the harsh days of winter and the dog days of summer. The moment that I came up with this completely reliable training partner, never again would I need prodding to hit the street, track, or trail on any given day.

Depending on the event that I was training for at a specific time, I would know the current world record in that event. I also knew that as time progressed the record would likely be broken only in increments from tenths of a second in the case of a middle-distance event to perhaps a minute or so in an event such as a marathon. I knew that if I worked smart and worked hard, I could close the gap by significant amounts in races ranging from the 800 to the marathon.

Each day or night that I went out and trained, I imagined the world's best at the event training hard in far-off exotic places, on long, lonely roads and trails, on the highlands and lowlands, and of course on the track. This would set my blood racing through my veins and arteries and sometimes would make the hair on my neck stand up in excitement and anticipation. I would imagine that they knew I was there in the far-off distance, seconds, minutes, and hours behind them in specific events but every bit as determined and professional as they were at their craft and closing in on them like a runaway freight train!

Beyond the Horizon

During the years when I was continuing to become faster—in my case up until 1998—this plan was bulletproof. During an eight-year span from 1990 to 1998, I closed to within approximately 35 seconds of the world record in the mile and to within less than 30 minutes in the marathon, a far cry in both events from where I began.

That is all well and good. But what about now, as I move toward my mid-40s and am no longer as fast as I was then? Now that I can no longer close in on the world record in any event, what to do now as a masters runner? Now that I am *beyond the horizon,* so to speak, as far as my fastest days go, or perhaps on the *dark side of the moon,* I still train as hard and as disciplined and smarter than ever, and I *still* use the same concept for daily inspiration as I did in previous years—with one difference.

Instead of trying to bring myself closer to the various records that I just discussed, which I cannot do, I continue each year to try to retard the slowing-down process. In other words, I try to remain as close to the current world record in the event that I am training for as I possibly can. That fact alone leaves me heading out the door every day with the crazy notion that the world record holder is still out there in some far-off exotic place, knowing that I am no longer coming at him like a freight train but still working harder and smarter than ever to prevent him from increasing the distance between us. Crazy maybe? But take it to the bank. This strategy is effective.

As I mentioned earlier in this chapter, there are a number of different issues to consider when discussing the topic of motivation. I have explained my fail-safe method for overcoming the day-to-day blahs and to help you stay focused and true to the task at hand. A case could be made that I have given you the tools to deal with the motivational difficulties associated with the psychology of training, but what about the physiology, the physical pain?

The Mocha and the Chocolate Chip Cookie

In the mid- to late 1990s, I was fortunate enough to train in Santa Cruz, California, under the guidance of Coach Greg Brock and a superlative group of training partners. Then, as now, Tuesday afternoons were the big group track day. Runners worldwide will tell you that track workouts are very demanding, both on the body and on the mind. Each interval, whether longer or shorter, has its own particular type of associated pain.

The longer interval tends to play on the mind as you imagine the impending physical pain that is about to consume you over time, a slow, mindless type of torture and blunt discomfort that is very wearing.

The shorter interval brings with it its own sense of anxiety and anticipation, as the runner knows that in very short order the physical demands will be very extreme and very painful: the heart pounding through the chest and the breaths as rapid and mechanical as a runaway freight train.

This is the way it has always been for me, even today, and it certainly was during those exciting track days in Santa Cruz. Back then, every Tuesday, at a time when I was still on the light side of the moon (meaning not yet at the peak of my running powers), was a love-hate fest. All morning I would be antsy, excited at the prospect of being challenged to my very limits at the track later that day. I couldn't wait for track time to come, and yet paradoxically, in a true microcosm of the sport of running, once the workout began, I couldn't wait for it to finish.

Other sports are not so. I doubt that in golf or tennis, for example, we are counting the seconds and minutes until the round or match is over. We runners all understand this aspect to running. I couldn't wait for the workout to finish, because it hurt. The enjoyment of hard running is not experienced in the moment but rather at the accomplishment, once ascendancy has been achieved. The satisfaction in the afterglow is what is so marvelous about this sport. The champion inside all of us beams in these moments. However, we have to get to this point first, and this is where the mocha and the chocolate chip cookie became so vital on this journey every week.

About a half mile from the track was a wonderful little coffee shop called the Surf City Coffee Company. Some of the group would head to the cafe after our workout and cool-down were complete, and we would treat ourselves to whatever was our fancy. For me, every week I would order a tall, nonfat mocha and a giant homemade chocolate chip cookie, the size of a saucer, and oh, they complemented each other so well and tasted so great.

However, the importance for me was not so much in their consumption but in their anticipation. The sum of their significance was greater than the parts. During the recovery segments of the workout each week, I would think about the mocha and cookie and would often discuss the upcoming sojourn to Surf City after the workout with my partners. The net effect was relaxation, and that is what this is all about.

Projecting my mind ahead to a relaxing time enjoying the mocha and the cookie with my heart rate returned to resting levels, dry clothes, and lively banter riding on the crest of running highs would remind me that the pain of the workout was finite. It was not indefinite; it would end, and there was life and fun thereafter.

To some this may seem obvious, even corny, but to me it often served as the very lifeline and raison d'etre that allowed me to negotiate the increasing fatigue and pain and handle the next interval.

Long-Term Frustration Worse Than Short-Term Pain

I am not a huge fan of fear serving as a motivator, but there is a place and a time for it, and there is no doubt that fear can be a very powerful force. It can be debilitating and very negative. Spending time during a workout or race focusing on the fear can in some cases spur the athlete on, motivated by fear itself to finish, just to bring an end to the pain. It does not work for everyone. Negativity can become all consuming.

Don't spend time thinking, *I cannot handle the pain anymore. I wish I weren't here. I wish I were sitting down eating an ice cream or reading a book. I am not going to make it. I wish my friends had not talked me into this race.* These are powerful negative influences and forces all designed to take you away from the positive of focusing on the task at hand, namely, the workout or race. You have come too far and trained too hard to let the negative get the better of you. Sure, the workouts hurt, but if you succumb to the negative, then yes, the short-term physical pain and mental anguish will be extinguished; but the associated frustration from giving in or quitting will not, and you will have to deal with that for days, weeks, and possibly even for months and years later. Therefore, my advice is this: when pain and doubt come, ask yourself whether you would rather deal with the short-term pain and anguish or suffer the indignity of self-frustration and doubt in the long term?

When doubts come, focus on the application of the biomechanics advice contained within this book.

Pursue Success and Run Free

You set the bar high for yourself. That is why you are a competitive athlete. The higher the importance attached to the outcome of a workout or race performance, the higher the level of anxiety associated with that performance. However, I have the antidote to *negative self-doubting,* which will allow you to pursue success and not to train or race in fear of failure. Pursuit of success is the opportunity that we allow ourselves to strive for excellence, unencumbered by the pressure of attaching self-worth and value to a given performance. It is about declaring your intent when asked to fully commit to a specific goal or goals appropriately based on recent results from training.

We do not base our fitness or performance on one workout or race. Rather, we take a look at trends over time so that we can make rational assessments about our performances and training in case adjustments need to be made—but we separate our identity from our results at all times. It is about having contingency plans should legitimate adjustments have to be made within a given performance and remaining positive as best we can at all times.

We are not a better person if we have a great race or a worse person if we come up short of our goals. There is no dishonor in coming up short, only in not trying. Pursuit of success is understanding that our weaknesses and failures are opportunities from which to improve by making corrections. Pursuit of success is not blaming others for our shortcomings but having strong enough self-esteem to accept responsibility for setbacks or losses. Pursuit of success is enjoying the journey and taking pride in your determination, courage, and commitment to compete regardless of the outcome. It is understanding that external extreme conditions such as heat and humidity will affect performance and that accepting this is not about losing face.

Pursuit of success is enjoying and acknowledging the past but differentiating it from the present as we become older and as time catches up with us. In other words, compete with your present self, not with the you from yesterday. Pursuit of success is about effective preparation in a sequential, planned, and rational manner leading to specific short-, mid-, and long-term goals. Pursuit of success is about good sportsmanship and the encouragement of others, including your adversaries, and it is about research in increasing your knowledge of your chosen sport. It is about following a well-balanced lifestyle, including appropriate health checkups, injury prevention, and management; nutrition, hydration, sleep, stress control; and a much overlooked off-season to achieve physiological and psychological restoration.

Athletes must be self-reliant. They may have a coach, friend, or parent on the sideline, but within the lines—in the trenches, so to speak—the only one they can turn to in the heat of battle is themselves. Very few of us will be Olympic athletes, Olympic champions, world champions, and world record holders. Therefore, as I see it, that leaves us with a clear, definable path. Our mission must be to work toward closing the gap between where we are today and those who have set the very highest marks in our sport.

While it is true that within the spirit of competition there are often times when we are looking to beat an individual or individuals. At the end of the day, unless this is on the world stage challenging for Olympic gold or a world record, what really matters is how we compete against our ultimate competitor, the person in the mirror—ourself!

A huge part of the attraction of sport and competition is that the outcome is unknown, and curiosity is a wonderful and natural human trait. Being an athlete and measuring ourselves against the unknown is a powerful and seductive proposition to see whether we can use every ounce of energy, strength, and skill to produce the result that we have been dreaming of.

What truly matters in relation to the fastest times, the highest or longest jumps or throws, or the highest scores is narrowing the gap to the closest margin between them and us. In doing so, we maximize our performance to its highest level, maximize every last drop of our talents to be able to say that we left nothing on the table, no stone unturned in pursuit of success. If we achieve this, if we extract the efforts and subsequent performances to take our body to its very limits, then and only then can we say that we pursued and achieved success regardless of the outcome of the jump, throw, run, swim, bike, or match. Beyond this point, it is a matter of DNA and genes, which is out of our control.

We must pursue and define success as maximizing everything we have within our control.

When we follow all of the aforementioned pursuit-of-success guidelines, then we can train and race unencumbered by the pressure of valuing and identifying who we are with the outcome of the performance. Setting ourselves free in this fashion is very motivating, as we become liberated to pursue all of the goals we have set forth for ourselves without attaching our self-worth to the outcome. In short, we are free to be highly motivated to pursue success without worry of fear of failure.

CHAPTER 10

Fueling the Fire

The subject of nutrition is perhaps the most confusing and frustrating aspect of training and living, period! I believe that this is caused by misinformation, inaccuracy, and quite often pure and simple intent to mislead. What follows is, I hope, a basic, real-life, in-the-trenches explanation of why we are what we eat and why proper fueling is essential to performance as a runner.

Food and the Body

Generally, the human body does not like to be stressed. For this reason, when stress is applied to the body (in the form of exercise), it responds by improving itself. During poststress recovery, the body functions in self-adjustment mode, rebuilding itself to be even stronger than before. It's almost as if little elves come out at night while you are sleeping and rebuild the castle so that it is better prepared for the task at hand next time around. Your rebuilt body will now be able to cope with that particular level of stress and discomfort in a much more comfortable and relaxed way.

Similarly, the human body is not in favor of giving up large amounts of fat. It works on the principle that the last meal you ate may be the last meal it will receive in a while. One of the body's primary functions is temperature regulation, particularly surrounding the vital organs—so it will give up on sugar, protein, and just about anything else before it will part company with its fat storage.

This is one of the key reasons why deprivation diets simply do not work. The body is way too clever, and it slows your metabolism down to a snail's pace in order to preserve precious energy, that is, stored fat. If you exercise at the same level on a consistent basis, your chess match will have reached a stalemate. Your body will have become extremely efficient at handling the workload placed upon it, burning the least amount of energy that it can get away with. This is why you need to exercise at varying intensities, continually challenging the body to reinvent itself by becoming fitter and stronger so that it increases its capacity to handle greater workloads. Then you need to feed the beast enough food so that it doesn't panic, thinking it is not going to get enough fat! Thus, the cycle continues. Let's review it from the body's perspective.

My Life (My Body) Living With "Human"

"I am being challenged (exercised). I am uncomfortable. I don't like this. I have to become lighter so that I can accomplish this new task as efficiently as possible—so that I am comfortable. Ah! But to achieve that, Human will starve me, a double whammy (extra stress and less food), so I will give up everything else—protein, carbohydrates, tissue—give it all up so that I can keep my fat reserves for warmth. Then when I become comfortable at the task, I can stabilize my metabolism and become very efficient. I can sneer at Human, as he is now exercising at a comfortable level for me. I can achieve the new task with my slower metabolism while still retaining decent levels of fat.

"What's that? Human is upping the intensity. Hmm, a chess match, eh? OK, back to regenerating myself, improving my performance so that I am comfortable. Still, I wish I was lighter. Well, better give up some more sugar and muscle to jettison some weight, make myself lighter. I cannot afford to give up those fat stores; who knows what Human will be up to next, exercising me like a mad dog on one hand and doubling up with a low-calorie diet on the other. I'll show Human.

"But wait a minute, what's this? Now Human is feeding me good-quality food and in generous amounts, with decent amounts of carbohydrates and proteins, good vitamins for chemical stabilization, and minerals for my bones and other important chemical reactions, and best of all enough fat (the good kind) to satisfy my needs. Now I feel balanced. Now if I have to perform harder and harder tasks (workouts) with adequate recovery/ rebuilding times—but I receive enough of the fuel I need—well, then, to be lighter, to be more efficient and comfortable during the chess match, I can afford to burn some fat.

"Burning some fat will help me weigh less so that I am more comfortable under stress. Since Human is feeding me the proper nutrition for survival, in sufficient amounts for me to retain as much as I need to protect my organs, then I guess it won't hurt to give up a few pounds of fat. Checkmate! Now, I am a lean, mean, running machine!"

That is it, runners. There may be more-scientific descriptions, mostly designed to confuse you. I dare say that there are more eloquent descriptions of the combined effects of training and nutrition, but they can be very hard to follow (mostly written by scientists who do a great job but may not really understand the mind-set of an athlete). Nor do they seem to understand the nutrition confusion that is out there—the fundamental lack of understanding of how the physiology of the human body works as it pertains to exercise and being fed. I hope that with my breakdown from the body's perspective, a few of these questions may have been answered and clouds of confusion lifted!

It Starts With the Shopping Cart

As an athlete who at the time of writing is approaching his 44th birthday, I find that intelligent nutritional choices play an even more integral role than they perhaps did 15 to 20 years ago. Although I am not academically trained in nutrition, I have been an experiment of one in terms of nutrition for performance for many years now. This trial-and-error experiment brings with it a great deal of experience over the years. I bring a simple, common sense approach to this subject both for me and for many of my runners.

It starts with the shopping cart. While there are many distractions at the grocery store designed to lead us astray from sound nutritional choices, there really is no excuse in America for not purchasing top-quality foods. There is an abundance of wonderful foods from all ethnicities available in villages, towns, and cities across America. Many communities such as my former hometown of Santa Cruz, California, offer farmers markets each week where you can purchase organic produce at extremely reasonable prices, sans pesticides, ranging from beets to bok choy and from milk to macadamia nuts.

In major supermarkets, there is a perpetuated fallacy that precooked dinners are time efficient and therefore save you time. The former may be true, but the latter is false. There is no reason at all that they should save you time.

Simple, nutritional, home-cooked meals can be prepared efficiently and afford you all the vitamins and minerals that you need for the active lifestyle of a performing athlete.

The first rule when you hit the grocery store is to not go there on an empty stomach, when you are extremely hungry and when you may succumb to all the refined sugars and trap foods that are offered. Better to go shopping on a satisfied stomach when more rational purchases can be made, such as healthy choice breads, cold cuts, fruits, vegetables, legumes, meats, and fish.

In the myopic world in which I live, major weight loss is not that prevalent; however, taking me and my runners during the course of the year from training weight to racing weight is very common.

To this end, on some levels it could be argued that just as it is harder for the 2:10 marathoner to reach 2:08 than for the 4:10 marathoner to reach 3:59, it is harder for the conditioned athlete to lose 2 to 3 pounds to be race ready for a middle-distance event than for someone 30 to 50 pounds overweight to lose some or all of that weight.

However, with that said, I am convinced that the protocols and planned nutrition design that I suggest work for all levels of athlete. Once again, it reinforces the importance of following the principles of the competitive athlete on many levels to achieve all-around success, both in performance and in health.

Sensible Daily Nutrition Options

This is a good time for me to offer an example of some sensible daily nutrition options.

Breakfast

Breakfast is really important to set the tone for the day. Here are my recommendations:

- One glass of water
- One to two glasses of orange juice
- Oatmeal or other type of cereal with low fat, skim, or soy milk. You can also add wheat germ as an excellent source of certain minerals and vitamins. Fruit can also be added.
- A bagel or toast with some jelly and peanut butter is fine too.
- Recommended one to two times per week: scrambled eggs with whites or an omelet for added protein.
- In the summer, fresh-fruit smoothies are excellent for breakfast.

Lunch

Lunch is an important opportunity within your day to maintain proper nutrition levels.

- Tuna sandwich
- Cheese and avocado sandwich
- Tortilla with beans/cheese
- A fresh-fruit smoothie with a piece of toast with peanut butter and jam
- A salad with a few nuts for protein
- Water

Dinner

Dinner is for the most part the last opportunity of the day to provide the required nutrients your body needs for regeneration during the sleeping hours.

- Light pasta with vegetables and shrimp
- Fish (salmon or swordfish), fresh vegetables, and/or whole wheat pasta
- A meal-size salad, such as salad nicoise
- Good hearty soups such as split pea and lentil, or other legumes or beans, such as kidney beans
- Veggie burger with baked potato or another starch such as brown rice
- For dessert, yogurt, fresh fruit, or sorbet

Snacks

For midmorning, I recommend dried fruit such as cranberries or half of an energy bar. A few graham crackers are great. Drink glasses of water through the morning. Nuts such as peanuts or almonds serve as a healthy, nutritious snack.

For midafternoon, I recommend fruit or dried fruit, or the other half of the energy bar. Yogurt is great or cheese. Peanuts or almonds also make for great snacks.

Finally, drink a minimum of 50 ounces of fresh water each day.

Bonus Pointers

Add some extra vegetables to your salads, especially red, green, yellow, or orange bell peppers, an excellent source of vitamin C. Add eggplant as a dinner vegetable. Baked potato and sweet potato or yams are excellent sources of antioxidants. Red beets, avocado, and nuts on a salad are very good too, full of nutrients and antioxidants to help fight off the breakdown of muscle cells from training.

Rice and leafy green vegetables like bok choy, spinach, and kale are all excellent sources of calcium and other minerals.

Don't Forget Your Minerals

Minerals such as magnesium, calcium, and potassium are particularly important. You need plenty of iron, but you also need vitamin C to help absorb the iron.

Magnesium comes from many sources and is a vital mineral for muscle control and central nervous system function. Wheat germ is an excellent source along with dried bananas, leafy green vegetables, dark chocolate, beet greens, legumes, and nuts. Calcium is also important for strong bones and muscle contraction and relaxation. Important sources of calcium are leafy green vegetables, sardines, cheese and other dairy products, pistachios, pinto beans, collard greens, tofu, chicken, beef, and salmon.

Good sources of potassium, for nerve function and fluid balance, are citrus fruits and bananas, apricots, raisins, almonds, whole milk, salmon, and chicken.

Eat salmon, swordfish, mahi-mahi, tuna, or sushi once a week as an excellent source of iron, critical for optimal health and performance. Iron carries the red blood cells in the form of hemoglobin to transport oxygen to the working muscles. Fish such as salmon, tuna, and swordfish is also an excellent source of omega-3 and omega-6 acids, which are the building blocks that help to replenish our muscle tissue.

What to Avoid

In the grocery store, stay away from the center aisles where the soda, candies, and refined sugars are all displayed. Stay to the outside aisles where you will find the fresh fruit, vegetables, legumes, breads, meats, fish, and cheeses.

Sodas are particularly abhorrent and completely abused in the United States. Most distressing is the number of children who pound sodas on a daily basis.

Most disturbing is the artificial sweetener aspartame, found in most diet, sugar-free, and diabetic products. Research has concluded that many serious side effects and symptoms are associated with its ingestion. The secondary danger is that many people assume because the package may contain the words "sugar free," that it is a license to ingest voluminous quantities, which is simply not true. The majority of products that contain aspartame carry empty calories such as processed flour, which can lead to obesity or being overweight because the body metabolizes these empty calories as fat.

Educating Our Children About Food

We need to educate children at a very early age and encourage them to drink water, milk, and natural fruit juices. As children grow older, certain sports drinks ingested at appropriate times such as Gatorade are fine, too, for hydrating purposes.

I am delighted that many schools, towns, boroughs, and states are outlawing the displaying and selling of sodas in schools today. There is simply no need for it, and the parents must be held accountable.

At my older son Luke's school, it amazes me to see the number of parents who send their child/children to school with very poorly planned lunches containing sodas, chips, cookies, and candy. Often my wife will overhear a parent say, "Well my child won't eat anything else," or "All they want is macaroni and cheese."

I blame this squarely on the parents. Neither of our children eats junk food or drinks sodas. If they want a dessert, they have to earn it by eating a well-balanced, nutritious meal, and then they can have a fruit-based popsickle.

Eating is a learned behavior. Parents simply do not reinforce the word "no." That is to say, they give in way too early to the child to keep the peace. There is no reason for this. Too many children are exposed to junk food at a very early age because it is time-efficient or convenient. As I said, eating is a learned behavior. If you gradually expose your children to healthy choices at an early age, they will acquire the taste for them.

They must understand that you are not running a restaurant out of your home. "This is tonight's dinner; if you do not eat it, that's fine. The next meal is breakfast." This isn't mean. It's just firm, and they will soon get the message.

Teach them about the origin of what they are eating, such as corn or eggplant from New Jersey, strawberries or artichokes from the Salinas Valley of California, oranges from Florida, or apples from Washington. Make meals a geographic experience to make it interesting, and teach them about the value and importance of nutritious items. We talk to our children about foods from around the world to tie in the food with the culture from which it originates. They love it, and this greater perspective makes the food and the mealtime experience much more interesting for them.

Competitive and Racing Shape

My athletic life is designed around two premises: competitive-preparation shape and racing shape. I work hard training throughout the year to prepare for competition, and as such I keep myself to a level of conditioning at all times that allows me to transition to an even higher level whenever necessary to compete for a specific period of time (season). In my case, it is usually an indoor or outdoor track season that lasts a few weeks at a time.

From a nutritional perspective, this is where the aforementioned comment comes into play: *It is harder for the 2:10 marathoner to reach 2:08 than for the 4:10 marathoner to reach 3:59. It is harder for the conditioned athlete to lose 2 to 3 pounds to be race ready for a middle-distance event than for someone 30 to 50 pounds overweight to lose some or all of that weight.* Not that I was ever a 2:10 marathoner, but my body is constantly at a low enough body-fat percentage that losing 2 to 3 pounds is challenging, and I need an effective plan to achieve the goal.

Racing shape is the reason that I must lose the 2 to 3 pounds. Racing the middle-distance events as I do is extremely challenging at the best of times but none more so than as a masters runner, and weight plays a very important role. It is important to race at the fulcrum, where you can be as light as you can without sacrificing strength. Excess weight, even to the tune of 2 to 3 pounds, will slow the runner down as ground forces are increased. While it is important for me to optimize my weight for racing season, I do not believe it's healthy for me to remain there for the duration of the year. This is tough on my immune and thermal regulation systems.

So, how do I achieve this change in weight in a safe, healthy, and effective manner without compromising strength and/or muscle tissue in any way? I follow these golden rules:

- Eat a good breakfast.
- Eat small, nutritious meals throughout the day.
- Drink plenty of fresh water.
- Avoid all nonnutritious snacks such as candy, cakes, cookies, and ice cream.
- Do not ingest anything except water or green tea after 6:30 P.M.

That is it, simple as 1-2-3. It works every time for me, and it is safe, effective, and will work for you.

What About the Mocha and the Chocolate Chip Cookie?

At the risk of contradiction, while I advocate very sound daily nutritional habits, as evidenced in this chapter, you may be wondering why I also advocate the reward system of the mocha and the chocolate chip cookie in Chapter 9. The answer is good old-fashioned common sense. As long as the majority of our daily intake is sound from a nutritional perspective, then there is nothing wrong if we stray from the hard line on occasion. To the contrary, I believe that a little reward can be motivating. It is all about balance. We do not have to be saints when it comes to our daily routine. I am able to separate what my daily requirements are from the psychological aspects of what the mocha and chocolate chip cookie represent during a very hard track workout. In essence, the sum of the representation of the chocolate chip cookie and mocha is far greater than the parts! I ask you to employ the same common sense.

CHAPTER 11

Don't Exercise . . . Train

Up until this point in the book, I have identified and discussed the basic elements involved in increasing your efficiency and economy as a runner. In addition, you now have an effective and time-efficient strength-training program to complement your running. What follows in this chapter is the discussion of some of the other important components of a well-balanced training program. By the end of the chapter, the phrase "don't exercise . . . train," should become clear.

Training . . . Not Exercising!

Not exercising—a strange recommendation indeed. Allow me to explain.

While I accept that even without a structured training regimen, regular workouts at your local health club are better than daily visits to a burger house, they are not enough to guarantee success in reaching your fitness goals over a long period of time, namely your lifetime.

I do not mean to suggest that in order to achieve a high degree of physical fitness, you must be an aspiring Olympian: not at all. I am simply suggesting that whether you are starting a physical fitness program for the first time or restarting one after 20 years of inactivity, you should *follow the proven physiological principles of training that a qualified coach would use in training an aspiring Olympian*. In coaching my age-group (amateur) runners, I always try to instill in them the importance of viewing themselves as athletes. If you are willing to forgo the easier option of the recliner in front of the television, get yourself out in all kinds of weather for a specific period of time or distance, and measure yourself against the clock, then you are deserving of the title "athlete." This title is not exclusive to those blessed with enough speed to challenge for an Olympic medal. Whatever your age or fitness level, carry yourself as an athlete and make sure you train as an athlete would train!

Exactly how does an athlete train? Well, the ruling principle is as follows: Optimal Stress followed by Optimal Recovery = Optimal Performance. This is known as the training effect and applies just as much to the novice as to the elite athlete. Athletes refer to this as the "hard-easy" method of training.

For example, when we perform a medium- to high-intensity exercise task, such as an up-tempo run, a specific stress is placed on the body that is equal to that intensity. After the task is completed, we immediately go into recovery mode, and depending on the intensity and duration of the task, the recovery period could be several hours to several days. During the course of a seven-day training period (often referred to by coaches as a microcycle), a hard training session will be followed by a decrease in fitness over the subsequent 24 hours as the body recovers and regenerates. This regeneration involves a combination of appropriate rest, good nutrition (taking in high-quality carbohydrates, proteins, and fats along with essential minerals and vitamins), proper hydration, and light training. This light training might include active isolated stretching and an easy run to assist with muscle soreness and the promotion of blood flow and suppleness throughout the body. The resulting effect is that the human body will rebound stronger and fitter than it was prior to the hard training day.

An important point to make here is that even though there are many factors to be considered in training the human body (such as training conditions, climate, and injury status), as a general rule, if the hard-day, easy-day theory is followed, the athlete is afforded a greater chance of success. On the other hand, if one hard day is followed by another hard day, then the regeneration or recovery period will be seriously impaired.

Yes, there are some exceptions to this rule, mainly having to do with the training of elite athletes for competition. These cases notwithstanding, it is extremely inadvisable for either the novice or the age-group runner to make a habit of putting in consecutive hard training days. To do so will prevent the steady recovery and regeneration that are essential for the continued climb up the fitness ladder through the body's physiological preparation for the next hard training session. Without this recovery, the results inevitably lead to overtraining, injury, and poor health.

For all the above reasons, don't just exercise. Train!

The Chess Match and the Plan

In chapter 9, I discussed motivation and the fact that extrinsic motivational factors such as wanting to look good or wishing to please someone else very rarely, if ever, work over a sustained period of time. With no plan of action, you will inevitably reach a plateau, frustration will set in, enjoyment will be reduced, and the goal will be abandoned. Even with the best of intentions, it's easy to get caught in this rudderless trap time and time again.

How to avoid the trap? Try thinking of your training in terms of a chess match. In this match, your body is always awaiting your next move, after which it can react accordingly. The knowledge and understanding of the nature of this chess match are the intangible elements separating the athlete from the weekend warrior or workout rat. The weapon that is used by the athlete to win the chess match is known as periodization, or the training plan.

"Periodization" is a term that appears regularly in texts on running and is used extensively in high school and college programs as well as at the club and professional levels. To some extent, it is an elitist term meaning "to train for a defined period of time with a beginning, middle, and end." Basically it means methodical, organized training for a predetermined, clearly defined period of time, allowing for the appropriate adaptation to stress (training), and leading to a goal event. This goal event might be the completion of a local race or a circuit of your neighborhood block, by a specific date.

For you to achieve success as an athlete—in other words, to achieve the benefits of long-term health and fitness—periodization, or a training plan, is the key. Break down short-, mid-, and long-term goals into bite-size amounts—the plan must contain specific daily goals. That way each day leads to the next, each week leads to the next, and each training cycle leads to the next, all the way up to the main goal. Once the goal (a race, perhaps) has been undertaken, there is an appropriate recovery period, then new goals are set, and the cycle begins again.

It is the progressively challenging nature of the goals, each requiring the body's appropriate adaptation, that will keep you continually reaching for new levels of success. Particularly motivational will be the short-term goals, and even when you fall short of a goal from time to time (as we all do), they will keep you motivated as you search yourself for a way to achieve that missed goal in the next attempt. This motivation, however, will not endure if you are training for the wrong reasons, as mentioned in chapter 9. In these cases, adherence is really in jeopardy, and more often than not, the training ceases.

What follows are a description and discussion of the major elements of an effective training plan. One quick note: because this book primarily covers the biomechanical aspects of running, I do not intend to cover all the aspects of cardiovascular training. Comprehensive information on human performance as affected by training the cardiopulmonary system can be found in many books on performance physiology such as the previously referenced *Training Distance Runners* by Martin and Coe.

Plan Element #1: The Training Log

A training log serves as a mine of information that can be used for diagnostic purposes with regard to our running, giving immediate feedback on the current state of body and mind. Without it, we are traveling blind: we have no records to remind us of how we got here and no compass to keep us on a course to our destination. With it, we can look at our history and make any necessary adjustments to help us along the way toward our goal. Reasonably priced training logs (usually in the $8 to $10 range) are available at all good running stores and sports outlets. They are often packed with training tips and pace charts that may help you toward your goal.

Plan Element #2: Short-Term, Midterm, and Long-Term Goals

These goals will be the foundation of your success:

Short-Term Goals

Time frame: Goal within one to two weeks.

Examples: Completion of a local race or one continuous loop of your neighborhood.

Midterm Goals

Time frame: Goal within two to six months.

Examples: To run a local race without stopping or to break a certain time for one mile on the track.

Long-Term Goals

Time frame: Goal could be from within six months to several years.

Examples: Completion of a marathon, walking a charity walk over several days, or training for the next Olympics.

As far as your goals are concerned, the possibilities are infinite, but it is the long-term goal that glows in the distance, while the short- and midterm goals light up the path along the way.

Plan Element #3: Training Periods

Unit

A specific interval or workload within a training session.

Session

A single or individual training session.

Microcycle

A shorter segment of your training program, typically seven days.

Mesocycle

An intermediate segment of your training program, often allowing enough time for one adaptation period (the length of time required, physiologically speaking, to benefit from a given workout). This is typically 14 to 21 days.

Macrocycle

A longer period of time often described as your training season. For example, a cross-country season or summertime racing season for 5K/10K races or, very often, the overall training period leading up to and including a half-marathon or marathon race. Typically two to three months and sometimes longer.

Plan Element #4: High-Quality or Up-Tempo Workouts

As previously mentioned, success in training comes from a combination of hard and easy days. I want to examine the terminologies of some of these up-tempo runs so that we can see which type of run falls into which category.

Aerobic Conditioning

This would be your easy day, a fun run with no requirement for running at a fast pace. It is conversational and can range in duration from 30 minutes to three hours depending on racing goal, location in training period, and ability. This run is designed to improve the body's ability to withstand the impact forces of running and to improve its efficiency at metabolizing stored fat for fuel.

Interval Training

A series of faster repetitions (usually at a set race pace or paces) for a predetermined distance and/or time followed by a predetermined recovery period by time and/or distance. For example, 10 repeats of 400 meters at 5K race pace with a 60-second jog between each repeat.

Fartlek Runs

Fartlek (the Swedish word for speed play) is an up-tempo or higher-intensity workout randomly selected over varying distances, times, and paces. The length of time of the fartlek run usually ranges from a matter of seconds to a couple of minutes.

Anaerobic Conditioning

All endurance events have both aerobic and anaerobic energy contributions. Anaerobic production has two sources:

1. Alactate, which is maximal-force running: an energy system that endures for eight to nine seconds.

2. Anaerobic glycolytic, which is an energy source that occurs above 65 percent $\dot{V}O_2$max. $\dot{V}O_2$max is the highest rate of oxygen utilization that can be achieved during maximal levels of exercise. Research has shown that this can be improved with endurance training.

Training between 65 and 85 percent $\dot{V}O_2$max is termed "training at your lactate threshold." Specific running at these intensities will improve the breakdown of glycogen as a substrate (a fuel source for energy metabolism). This allows the runner to go farther and faster before being hindered by the accumulation of lactic acid, a byproduct of anaerobic energy production.

Hill Repeats

A series of faster repetitions (usually at a set race pace or paces) for a predetermined time and/or distance followed by a predetermined recovery time and/or distance. They can range in length from 30 seconds to several minutes. The shorter the repeat, the higher the intensity of the running. Hill repeats build tremendous strength in the muscles and the skeletal system, increasing the power output of the heart along with improving the economy and efficiency of the stride.

An example might be 10 repeats of a 30-second acceleration up a hill at 5K race effort with a 60-second jog between each repeat. Hill repeats usually last for a cycle of four to six weeks. There may be as many as two to three cycles of four to six weeks, run once per week in a macrocycle, depending on the level of athlete.

Which Plan Is Right for Me?

Finding the right training program for you is essential if you are to succeed at your sport. Many resources are available to get you started on creating your own plan. You can refer to books such as *Better Training for Distance Runners*, as previously mentioned, or *Workouts for Working People* by legendary Ironman triathletes Mark Allen and Julie Moss. Contact your local running club, running store, or running coaches for this kind of information. Finally, you can use the Internet, which can be a tremendous running resource.

Use these sources to look at your goals and work out your plan. Remember that no matter what your goals might be, your plan should closely match your current ability but should also incorporate an ample degree of challenge. Make sure that your goals can be achieved only through consistent training. If the plan is too easy, you will not maximize its benefits; if it is too hard, then at best you may lose motivation and at worst you run the risk of injury.

A good basic plan should incorporate aerobic-type running, speed work, strength running, strength training, and work on your range of motion and flexibility. There are a couple of hard and fast rules to consider in your plan. Do not increase your mileage by more than 5 percent per week, and do not run more than 10 percent of your weekly mileage as speed work (novices) or up to 20 percent for advanced runners.

Three Sample Training Plans

What follows are three seven-day training plans provided for three of my athletes. As you will see, their schedules vary widely, but the basic elements remain the same.

Each of these three schedules represents a plan, an agenda designed to lead from one day to the next, from one week to the next, and from one mesocycle to the next until ultimately arriving at the main goal of each athlete. After that main goal has been attempted, and regardless of whether it was attained, it is time for recovery and rest before embarking on the next challenge. This is how the cycle of training continues.

Sample Training Plan #1

NOVICE/INTERMEDIATE

Mesocycle #1, Week #1

The agenda for this mesocycle is consistency plus a very slight increase in endurance. Pay attention to your breathing rhythm as discussed. This will help you later on as the schedule becomes more complex. Our goal in weeks 1 to 3 is to hit 90 to 95 percent of the schedule. We are training via heart rate for phase 1. The key is to develop your body's ability to recover efficiently while on the move. This will be achieved through continuous steady-state (even pace) running at a moderate effort with little or no recovery.

MONDAY Off. Relax and stretch.

TUESDAY Easy 3.5 miles of relaxed running. Run tall and with good posture and good form, think about your mechanics, the way you carry your arms, and your relaxed breathing. Your heart rate should not build to more than 140 beats per minute (bpm) on this run.

WEDNESDAY Off. Relax, rest, and stretch today. Possible yoga class.

THURSDAY Morning run: 30 minutes. Keep heart rate under 140 bpm. Evening run: 30 minutes. Keep heart rate under 150 bpm.

FRIDAY Off. Stretch and hydrate.

SATURDAY At the track.
- 1-mile warm-up/cool-down (opposite direction, clockwise middle lanes, very easy pace).
- 1-mile strides (4 laps counterclockwise). Jog the turns, stride the straights in 25 seconds. This is to stimulate your central nervous system and to physiologically prepare you for the workout.
- The workout: 800 m in 2:05 per lap (8:20 mile pace); 400 m in 2:00 per lap (8:00 mile pace); 2,000 m in 2:08 per lap (8:32 mile pace); 400 m in 1:59 per lap (7:56 mile pace).
- Take a one-lap easy jog between each interval. Focus on good pacing and good breathing technique.

SUNDAY 7-mile run.
- Run tall, good posture, think about your mechanics.
- Keep your heart rate no higher than 140 bpm.

Sample Training Plan #2

ADVANCED FEMALE RUNNER RECOVERING FROM INJURY

Mesocycle #8, Week #1

Training schedule for a 30-year-old female runner, capable of running a sub-19-minute 5K. This runner is recovering from injury, so her schedule consists entirely of cross-training.

MONDAY Off. Relax, stretch, and hydrate.

TUESDAY 20-mile bike ride. Include 4 × 3-minute medium-intensity accelerations. Average heart rate should be 140 bpm, reaching 155 during accelerations. Leave time for a cool-down ride at the finish.

WEDNESDAY Elliptical machine, 30 minutes. Low intensity, paralleling an easy run. Keep the heart rate below 145 bpm.

THURSDAY In the pool.
Warm-up: 250 yards, then aqua jog 2 sets.

ACCELERATIONS	EFFORT	RECOVERY
1 minute	Mile	30 seconds
2 minutes	5K	30 seconds
3 minutes	5K	30 seconds
3 minutes	5K	30 seconds
2 minutes	5K	30 seconds
1 minute	Mile	End workout

Cool-down: 100-yard easy swim to cool down after aqua jog.

FRIDAY Elliptical machine, 40 minutes of easy training, paralleling a 40-minute easy run. Keep the heart rate below 145 bpm.

SATURDAY Tempo elliptical. 45 minutes total. Warm up for 15 minutes at a low intensity. Keep the heart rate below 130 bpm. Then do a steady-state tempo run, equating to 15 minutes of running at threshold effort (10K pace + 15 seconds per mile). Cool down for 15 minutes at the end of the tempo. Work on good posture and excellent breathing.

SUNDAY Bike for 90 minutes at a steady-state effort. Keep your heart rate below 145 bpm. Then hydrate, stretch, and rest.

Sample Training Plan #3

ELITE MALE

Mesocycle #4, Week #3

Training schedule for a 25-year-old elite male athlete, during the speed endurance and stamina phase of his training.

MONDAY   Off. Relax, stretch, and hydrate.

TUESDAY   At the track.
- Usual 2-mile warm-up and mile of strides.
- Workout: 4 × 150 m (at 22.5-second pace), with 50 m jog between each; then a 400 m jog; 7 × 1,000 m "in and out" pace, alternating each 200 m in 30 and 40 seconds, respectively.
- 400 m jog between sets.
- 4-mile cool-down.
- Maintain the .5 second tolerance per lap. Maintain excellent breathing and good controlled balance. Stay focused.

WEDNESDAY   Morning run: 6 miles easy running. Stretch and hydrate. Afternoon run: 4 miles midpace.

THURSDAY
- Jog to hill. 16 × 60 seconds @ 5K effort, 2-minute recovery.
- Return to track for 1 mile in 4:45.
- 4-mile cool-down.
- Pay close attention to relaxation of upper body. Drive the arms and generate efficient knee drive.

FRIDAY   10-mile recovery run. Stretch, hydrate, rest, and get to sleep early.

SATURDAY   Tempo run. Warm up 2 miles easy. Move smoothly to 5:45 pace for 1 mile, slow to 6:30 pace for 2 minutes, return to 5:30 pace for remainder of fourth mile, then jog easy 2 minutes. Then run 10 × 20 seconds at 4:40 pace with a 30-second jog between. After the last one, jog 2 minutes, then run 3 miles at 5:15 pace. Cool down 2 miles to finish.

SUNDAY   75 to 80 minutes at low heart rate. Steady-state effort. Keep the heart rate below 145 bpm. Hydrate, stretch, and rest afterwards.

Following a race, I recommend one easy day of running per mile raced before attempting anything up-tempo. Thus your plan should specify three easy days following a 5K, six easy days following a 10K, 26 easy days following a marathon, and so on.

As I have said, use all the resources available to you in developing your own goals and your own training plan. (For more detailed information on how to receive personalized training schedules such as the examples in this book, you can either send an e-mail to *CoachGP@runningbuzz.com* or visit our Web site at *www.runningbuzz.com.*)

So, now we know that a training plan or cycle has a predefined period of time; contains short-, mid-, and long-term goals; and includes training at varying intensities in order to stimulate physical adaptation to its highest level. We can also feel very confident that with regard to our health and these training plans, all roads lead in the same direction, namely to a stronger and more-efficient heart. In fact, the benefits from this type of exercise include, among others, lower stress levels, improved cholesterol levels, reduced risk of heart disease, reduced blood pressure, reduced risk of Type 2 diabetes, decreased weight, and better body composition.

How far we choose to drive our training depends on many variables—genes, age, health history, diet, stress levels, climate, time, and motivation. No matter what type of athlete you are and no matter how you choose to plan your schedule, the principles of stress and recovery-type training will remain true. Remember Optimal Stress followed by Optimal Recovery = Optimal Performance, and you'll be positioning yourself to achieve all of your goals.

The Plan

We must be mindful of the fact that the human body is an intricate and amazing machine. If we want to improve that machine, there are no short cuts and no easy routes to success—just good, honest, and ultimately rewarding hard work. We must also take into consideration the established principles of training, whereby our workouts challenge us just enough to keep us coming back for more but not so hard that we risk injury and overtraining.

It is this sequential programming, the training in cycles, that allows our bodies to adapt and improve on a consistent basis, giving us a sneak preview with each new level into rewards yet unknown.

You might be wondering how best to make use of all this information. I recommend, in this order, that you set about creating good fueling habits, as outlined in chapter 10, and then move on to establishing your short-, mid-, and long-term goals. Once done, immediately start developing your own training plan as outlined in this book.

You can use either a computer program or one of the many versatile training logs available online or at your local running store. Remember that you need to build from week to week, incorporating hard and easy recovery training days.

Over several mesocycles (approximately three weeks of training to one mesocycle), what were formerly your hard days will become your current easy days, and your easy pace will eventually develop into what you once considered your intermediate pace. With the addition of some training races along the way, your workouts should continue to build all the way up to your main goal (completion of the macrocycle).

After the goal event is completed, you should enjoy a period of complete rest and recovery known as your off-season. During that time, you can plan out your next season and, with good judgment, you can determine what paces and distances you should begin with at the start of your next program. I recommend that you begin at the distances and intensities that you had reached at about two-thirds of your way through your previous season. This way you will be continuing to progress rather than beginning each season at the same level. This progression will afford you the opportunity to keep striving toward new levels of fitness and speed. Remember that as you become fitter and faster, so the increments of improvement become smaller and smaller, but the rewards are just as great.

What it all boils down to is this: Don't Exercise . . .Train.

CHAPTER 12

Training as an Athlete—True Stories

In the first edition of this book, I wrote about two of my athletes, David and Caroline, who served as beacons of inspiration in having overcome major obstacles to turn their lives around with the assistance of planned, methodical training, in addition to great drive and determination.

I mentioned that it was very difficult, having coached thousands of athletes, to single out the stories of only two. Some years later now, though, two new stories come to mind. These two athletes could not be more diverse in their sex, age, ability, and goals, yet they share a common thread of methodical, planned training methods and an intense desire to succeed.

Meet Muzz L.

At the time of writing, I have been working with Muzz for five years. Muzz is a molecular biologist in her 40s who lives on the East Coast and brings intense passion with her 5-foot-2-inch frame and determination to all aspects of her life, including her family, dogs, work, scuba diving, and of course her running and teammates.

One of the first things that Muzz mentioned in her initial contact e-mail was that she wanted to qualify for the Boston Marathon. In her age group, this would take a marathon under four hours. At the time that Muzz and I began working together, her best time was 21 minutes, 31 seconds away from her dream. By her own admission, her running form was poor, and as a result she experienced downtime from running with shin splints and plantar fasciitis.

We immediately set about the task, as I do with all of my athletes, of optimizing her running form by improving her foot-strike position and the angle of her arm carriage and by minimizing excessive torso rotation.

One of my objectives with Muzz was to introduce her to the track to develop her ability to control pace (an essential element to successful marathoning), to improve her mechanics, to develop her speed, to improve her ability to recover on the move (speed endurance), and to broaden her horizon as far as racing at varying distances from 400 meters up. Simply put, by becoming a better track runner and racer, she would become a much more complete and confident runner and racer.

It took us nearly two years to qualify Muzz for Boston, but qualify her we did.

It was and continues to be a great success story, with Muzz setting personal bests in numerous race distances along the way, including racing and setting personal bests at the famed New York Armory indoor track in New York City. Along the way, in addition to improving running form, we have worked on Muzz's range of motion and flexibility and her strength and conditioning program including, in more recent times, the incorporation of Russian kettlebell training.

I am an in-the-trenches type of coach, blue collar, if you will. That is to say, my own running career developed with on-the-fly learning, out in the field, not by studying what may or may not work in the laboratory. I made mistakes and learned on the streets, tracks, and trails, with true-life experiences, improvisations, and adjustments. I learned in that fashion, and I coach in the same way.

Here are real sections of e-mails between Muzz and me that provide some insight into her two-year progression from when we first began working together to the time that she realized her dream by qualifying for the Boston Marathon.

Muzz: "I want to qualify for Boston."

Muzz: "What motivates me: becoming the best I can. I don't know how good a runner I can be, but I want to find out. I want to qualify for Boston . . . and then I'd like to have a great race there. I'm looking forward to many future years of improving times. I'd like to win some medals along the way . . . local, regional, who knows? I want to enjoy the whole process as I go, knowing that I've done what I could to reach my personal best."

Coach GP: "You should know that my first marathon was a 4:41, and in eight years I (with extremely focused work and work ethics) took that to a 2:34 level . . . so believe me when I tell you that I know what it takes. I remember desperately wanting to qualify for Boston and finally achieving that dream of being at the starting line in Hopkinton. It is an incredible feeling, and we must get you there."

Six months into our coach-athlete relationship, Muzz ran her second marathon, our first together:

Muzz: "Hi, GP, I didn't make it by a long shot. I don't even want to look at the splits right now. The short story is I was about two minutes ahead of schedule at the half (running with the four-hour pace leader—trying to make use of a pack), and then somewhere over the next few miles, my hamstring felt like it just seized up. The decline was ugly, I just couldn't get comfortable, and I had to change the goal to finishing, which I did in 4:16 something. Obviously it was not the race I wanted or the race I know I have in me—by a long shot. When I finished, I felt like I wasn't disappointed because I'd at least made it, but right now I'm feeling pretty damn low. I think I'll just give this a chance to mix around in my mind for a while and then let it settle a bit."

Muzz: "OK, now that I've had a couple of hours to brood, I guess my conclusion is that I've sure made my share of mistakes, and in the end they cost me a chance at qualifying for Boston today. But that doesn't mean I can't learn from them and get there. I am not a quitter, and I've just got to climb back up on the horse. New York's six months away."

Muzz: "I am obviously disappointed with my performance yesterday, but it's hard to kick yourself too much when everyone you work with thinks you're a hero just for finishing a marathon. The way I figure it is that if you compare the joy I got from the last several months of training (even when it was really rough!) to the disappointment of a single day—even when that day is what you were aiming for all along—the joy crushes the disappointment in comparison. Besides, there will be another chance to reach my goal."

Six months later after our next marathon together, almost a year after we first started together:

> *Muzz:* "I am of course very disappointed in yesterday's outcome, but I felt I did what I could. I ran conservatively and followed our plan—up until the heat got the better of me. I felt like the energy just got sucked out. In my heart and mind, I am absolutely confident that on a better day our goal was completely within my reach, but as you say, the marathon is an unpredictable animal. I felt that my preparation was complete and well targeted and otherwise had me ready and primed to where I needed to be. We controlled for everything we could—but there are some things you can't control. I finished the race. It wasn't easy. Despite my best efforts to stay hydrated and keep cool, I got a little wobbly at mile 21 when I had to come to a dead stop for water, and at mile 24 I could hear the pounding of my feet in my head. I was never out of control, but to be honest, the wobbliness scared me a little—I'd already seen several people start going sideways and be stopped by medical or police—and a few who had already fallen. The funny thing is that even though my NJ time was 12 minutes faster, I thought I ran a better race, more in control, following the plan, calm and focused until external conditions threw me for a curve and forced me to retrench. Boston is still my dream, and I'll get there. I dreamed about it for 30 years before I made any marathon a reality, and I'm in striking distance fairly quickly. I can wait a little longer. Patience!
>
> *Coach GP:* "Your e-mail is well said and right on the money. We *will* get you to Boston!"

Almost a year later, as Muzz was on the cusp of racing our third marathon together in her attempt to qualify for Boston:

> *Coach GP:* "Muzz, you have trained really well. Once again it has been a pleasure to guide you toward this great goal. I wish you very well with your race. I will be thinking of you and I know you will do great! Let me know if you need anything. Boston, here you come!

The day after the marathon, two years after we first began together:

Muzz: "Hey, Coach GP, I am not sure you heard my last words to you on the phone yesterday, so I will repeat them. Thank you! We discussed lots about the race and will probably do so again, but just a few things: I can't say I felt particularly good or as if I were having a stellar performance, I think because I was all business . . . I don't think I have ever been so focused and in the moment. How I felt did not matter; I was qualifying, and that was it. That said, there were moments of tiredness and working through it, at mile 10 and mile 18, and probably some others. At about 21, I knew the legs were out of reserves but the will was there. At about 23, I wondered if I could actually pick it up (that's how we train!), but I knew I was in uncharted territory, I didn't want to pick it up then and risk bonking in the last mile, so the name of the game was *maintain*. Don't lose track of the goal: the Boston qualifier. So I just tried to stay steady. The last mile I was seriously tired but still able to hold the pace and finish strong. No sprint to be sure, but steady all the way."

Muzz achieved her dream of qualifying for Boston with a 3:58:39 marathon, 81 seconds under the required time.

Coach GP: "Muzz, great debrief. Thank you. You did it! I just laid out the road map. . . . I like your splits, especially last 10K. . . . The heart rate was just right, just below A\T. . . . We will use same formula for Boston but will do some more hill running. . . . That is for another day; I am thrilled and now just rest, heal your body, and bask in the glory. . . . Then it will be 'Muzz, what have you done for me lately?' . . . Nice coach, eh? Seriously, great work. . . . Hopkinton, here we come!"

What a thrill to work with and witness someone achieve her dream with hard work, coachability, and such drive and determination. Never has there been an athlete more deserving of success.

Muzz and I continue to work together as coach and athlete spanning the spectrum of races from 400 meters to the marathon.

Meet Owen B.

I began working with Owen in the summer before his junior year of high school. He had very little experience as a runner and at that time was more of an ice hockey player. He attended a two-day running seminar that I conducted and subsequently made the decision that he wanted to run cross-country. He was interested in working with me as his coach, but the problem was that his high school—although offering very little in the way of qualified, competent coaching and without proper facilities—frowned upon its runners receiving outside professional help. This was in spite of the fact that precedent had been set at the school, with other nonmainstream sport participants such as swimmers being given the green light to receive help from outside clubs.

Owen was a slight young man, about 5 feet 10 at the time and 120 pounds wet with an Art Garfunkel hairstyle. To be honest, he was so quiet and unassuming during the clinic that if his mother had not specifically asked me to meet with her and Owen at the end of the camp, I may not have recognized him a week later if I saw him on the street.

It was at this meeting that Owen and his mother expressed interest in seeking my help. I was reluctant at the time but did suggest that he attend one of my Saturday track sessions, where anyone in the community is welcome.

The following Saturday, Owen attended track. After he took a proper warm-up, I told him that I was going to assess his current fitness level by having him run a two-mile time trial, which he completed in a respectable yet unremarkable 13 minutes, 20 seconds—a time that would not place high in a girl's two-mile race at a high school dual meet.

Owen struck me as a polite, humble young man who showed a genuine desire to improve. I was not even remotely thinking that he would amount to much as a runner at this time, and there seemed little point in charging his parents' hard-earned money without prospects of a likely reward at the end of the day.

Since it was summer break and we were therefore unencumbered by the school calendar, I suggested that he could run with me on my recovery days to work on some basic aerobic development and that he could attend on days that I was running track.

At the time, I was very focused on training a standout collegiate runner from Colgate University who was preparing to go to California from the East Coast to join up with the Stanford Alumni Farm team under Coach Frank Gagliano.

As the first few days turned into the first couple of weeks, Owen began to develop his fitness, as you would expect, but again without raising any eyebrows. One very hot August day, I ran a midafternoon track workout with Xavier, the aforementioned athlete from Colgate. It was a tricky workout, especially given the very high heat index. It was a two mile, calling for a five-minute first mile, the next two laps recovering to 5:40 pace, and then returning to five-minute pace for the last 800 meters. My instructions to Owen were to construct the workout in the same sequence but at slower paces.

Sure enough, this is exactly what Owen did. To be honest, this was a coaching moment when I questioned myself. *Could he handle this workout, let alone finish it?* Yet, if I am honest with myself, my main focus that day was making sure that Xavier achieved the paces in the workout that I had mandated. As Xavier and I proceeded through the laps, I would take occasional glances back, and there was Owen, hanging on by his fingernails but not conceding, not giving up. Sometime after we finished a grueling two mile, here came Owen, finishing what he had started.

This is the moment when he earned my respect for the first time. His two-mile time that day in brutal heat was a good 90-plus seconds faster than the two-mile trial I had given him a few short weeks before. I know Xavier looked upon him differently after that day, almost as if he had earned his stripes. That was not the intention of the day but seemingly the way it turned out.

As dismissive of him as I was in the beginning because of the aforementioned school issues and never really considering him a long-term project, Owen began to ingratiate himself to me. He would call every night at 9:00 P.M. to discuss that day's workout and to get the instructions for the following day.

The next thing that I remember was that he showed up at track with a short haircut, no more the Art Garfunkel. This, to me, was all part of the growing-up process for Owen and the transition from young adolescent to serious athlete. I was particularly impressed with the way that my entire Jersey Stinger Saturday-morning track group took to him, specifically his politeness and unassuming attitude.

My friend and fellow coach, Tom Schaefer, would discuss Owen at coffee after these Saturday track sessions. However, at this stage, the discussions were more about his attitude than his untapped ability.

We began running longer Sunday runs on the boardwalk in Spring Lake, New Jersey. Owen's running form was still far from efficient. His arms were carried far too long and too straight with his hands almost at midthigh, reducing efficiency and the speed at which he could move them. The resulting lack of upper body power minimized his distance in flight. The result was that although blessed with a long, lean running body, Owen would land much too squarely on his heels, again reducing the speed at which the support leg would return into the leg cycle.

These Sunday runs included many of the better runners and triathletes in the area, and the paces would inevitably increase toward the last few miles. Owen would struggle to hang on, form ungainly and breathing hard, but hang on he would. At the end of these runs, not much was said of Owen. The tsunami that was to come was not yet on the horizon.

At the track, we continued to work on his running form, particularly the angle at which he carried his arms, his subsequent leg drive, and the resulting angle at which his front foot would strike the ground. We always worked on having Owen develop the perfect distance-runners' 90-degree angle between upper and lower arms, allowing for greater upper body power, improving knee drive, and thereby providing the forum for his front foot to land on his midfoot and sweep off the ground.

I did this with running drills to work on perfect running form and create exaggerated running movements to stimulate proper muscle-fiber recruitment and pattern sequencing. This was in addition to many 150-meter repeats at swift and progressive paces.

These 150-meter repeats are the perfect distance (half a turn and one straightaway on the track) for fast paces (faster than race pace) under control without incurring excessive lactate buildup. This distance and speed will also contribute to improved running mechanics. The desired speed of the interval can be tempered by the recovery. For example, if the stated recovery is 50 meters, then upon completion of the 150-meter interval, the runner jogs very slowly with perfect running form for the next 50 meters halfway around the turn and begins the next interval. This would be speed endurance and would be at a controlled, faster pace, 5K- or mile-type pace depending upon the agenda. At the right time of the season, the 150-meter intervals can be run where the runner completes the 150 meters, then jogs 250 meters to return to the starting point. Due to the increased recovery length, this speed interval will be lower in volume but faster in pace, ranging from 400- to 800-meter pace/effort.

As often happens when runners work on their form, overcompensations are made. This is fine. As a coach, just go with it; it will work itself out with proper guidance and instruction. This was the case with Owen as he moved his arms from down by his midthigh to up by his midribs. In this position, the levers are shortened so the arms swing faster around the shoulder joint. This means they put excessive stress on the shoulders and do not engage the larger back muscles, which are essential for efficient power. A good analogy here would be cycling along in a low gear with high cadence, not developing much power, as opposed to pedaling in a higher gear with lower cadence with increased power.

Soon it was time for our first cross-country season together. The two courses we would have to focus on would be the Sea Girt army camp, a huge piece of property occupied by the National Guard that at the eastern end nestles up against the beach and often receives a beating from the prevailing winds along the Atlantic Coast. Although situated on lowlands, the course is rutty with several turns and is seemingly at the mercy of the raw winds. This was the home course of Owen's high school.

The second course, Holmdel Park—part of the Monmouth County, New Jersey, park system—is a famed high school and collegiate cross-country course with great tradition. It is a course that over the generations has humbled many a fine athlete. It is inland off exit 114 on the Garden State Parkway, 40 miles south of New York City.

Holmdel boasts an incredibly tough, predominantly uphill, first mile with a particularly difficult first 600 meters up a grass hill that turns into an even steeper hill on a gravel path before finally leveling out and transitioning into a roller coaster for 300 meters or so. It also boasts "the bowl," which causes trepidation to just about every runner who has to negotiate this long downhill section of dirt road in the first half of the second mile, descending into this bowl-like setting winding through some reasonably level terrain before finally turning upward on a particularly nasty hill in the early stages of the second half of the second mile. At the very top of this hill, when your heart is in your throat and your legs are screaming, is a very steep last 15 meters or so with a left turn that flat out just tests your will. The first half of the last mile is generally easy with some turns before heading back into the woods and finishing the last 800 meters or so on a trail with a wicked, steep descent.

Many of our athletes are affectionately afforded nicknames such as Billy "the Kid" Kelly or Derek "the Rocket" Cardinale, and Owen was no different. He became known to me as OB1. Because his initials are O.B. and I grew up in the '70s as a Star Wars fan, I kept thinking of the legendary Jedi Knight, Obi-Wan Kenobi.

So OB1 and I would scout every inch of the Holmdel course, strategizing and discussing tactics of how best to race on the course.

Owen was soon dominating other schools in dual meets in this, his junior year at the army-camp course, seeming to set personal bests with every race.

By the end of our first cross-country season together, OB1 was no longer under the radar with the local media. He had made the necessary mechanical adjustments. He now had a well-placed arm carriage with palms alongside his hips and subsequent strong, fluid midfoot strike allowing him to use every inch of his tall, wiry frame. He was now becoming quite a running machine. He had the tools to endure increased physiological stress in workouts resulting in increased psychological capacity to handle greater physical stress with each session. In short, he was on an upward spiral, and the tsunami had arrived!

Owen made it all the way through to the New Jersey state meet that season, recording huge personal bests including a 16:21 on the Holmdel 5K course.

Through the winter of his junior year, we continued to work on his speed development, even working at the local health club on high-speed treadmills, which had the capacity to go up to 15.6 miles per hour. Owen doing sprints on these high-speed treadmills with his already tall and gangly body was quite a sight to see. With perspiration flying everywhere, I am not sure what the more subdued club members made of him. However, with frigid New Jersey winter temperatures outside and snow on the ground, we had to do what we had to do.

Things continued to get better and better with OB1, but like all athletes, he had down moments. He struggled during the Shore Conference indoor two mile at Princeton University and again later that year at the Shore Conference outdoor mile during spring track. Within the first few steps of that race, Owen had his heel stepped on, resulting in his shoe coming off at the end of the first lap. Determined to finish what he started, he kept running and came in dead last. Adding insult to injury was the damaged and bloodied foot he endured.

One of OB1's great assets is his ability to shrug off adversity and move on to the next challenge.

Remember Owen's initial 13:20 two mile, which he ran the first time on the track with me? Eleven months later, during the outdoor Shore Conference two mile, Owen improved his two-mile mark to 9:35. This will give you an idea of the talent and dedication he possesses. In the summer between his junior and senior years, we would return to those Sunday runs with the local triathletes and runners. Unlike before, when he was challenged in the latter stages of the run, Owen would drop them like hot potatoes. They were no longer in the same ZIP code. Owen had arrived!

His senior year of cross-country proved a great success, with OB1 making it all the way to the Foot Locker regional meet at Van Cortlandt Park in New York. However, the race that stands out in my mind was the Shore Conference race that year at Holmdel. An outstanding runner named Craig Forys was expected to win the race going away. I had great respect for Craig and his coach, Jim Schlentz. Craig was a dedicated young man, but I told Owen to respect him but not fear him. To this point, Craig had run much faster times than OB1, but I trusted in OB1's training. His times in training were becoming faster and faster, and he was due a big break-through. This would be the day. On a crisp, clear, East Coast fall day with the leaves sporting an array of gorgeous colors, the two young men hit the two-mile marker in first and second places with OB1 trailing by 30 meters. Over the next 500 meters, OB1 began to challenge the unchallengeable. Arguably this was the defining moment in Owen's high school career, when he truly believed he was everything that we believed him to be and when he truly believed that he belonged in this rarefied air of elite high school racing. The gap with 1K to go was down to 12 meters. Craig showed his class and held on to win the race, but Owen acquitted himself in fantastic fashion finishing second and improving his time on the Holmdel course to 15:53. This was one of the fastest times ever run on the course by a runner from his high school.

What was interesting about the timing of this race was that a few weeks before, a great friend of mine—Ronnie Holassie, a two-time Olympic marathoner for Trinidad—was staying at my home for a few days. One day, while I was running with Owen and Ronnie, Ronnie was imparting his running wisdom to OB1 in the early stages when the pace was easy, but the latter part of the run called for some hard accelerations. Owen and Ronnie took off heading south on the boardwalk in Spring Lake, leaving me in their wake. When I finally caught up with them after the run, it seemed that Owen was on cloud nine from experiencing what it was like to run with an Olympian. That one singular run seemed to carry him on a wave of confidence for the rest of the season, a season that culminated in a third-place finish at the state Meet of Champions behind Craig Forys and Jeffrey Perrella with another personal best of 15:51.

We returned to the high-paced treadmill workouts through the winter, but again there was a stumbling block during the climax of the indoor season. Before I was able to arrive in Princeton, Owen warmed up for his indoor two-mile race at the Shore Conference meet by running outside on the outdoor track in 20-degree temperatures. Owen did not realize the negative physiological impact this would have on his metabolism and on his pulmonary system.

After the race, he would come to realize! During extremely warm, or hot, and/or humid conditions, the brain signals the body to send blood to the surface to assist in the cooling-off process—heat dissipation through evaporation into the atmosphere. This is all part of the human body's very efficient metabolic system. However, there is a price for the runner and that is less available blood and therefore less available oxygen to the working muscles. In simplistic terms, this is the reason why our heart rates run higher and the effort to achieve specific paces is far greater than that experienced in moderate temperatures.

In a different way but with the net same result is the effect of the extreme cold—thermo regulation being one of the body's primary functions (i.e., to protect the temperature of the vital organs at all times). In extreme cold, a chain of metabolic events takes place, but again in simplistic terms there is constriction of blood skin vessels to minimize heat loss in addition to the shift of blood to the vital organ area. The net effect (as with the extreme heat scenario) is less blood and therefore less oxygen available to the working muscles. The bottom line with both extreme heat and extreme cold is that we have to work much harder to run paces that we could otherwise achieve with much less effort during temperate or moderate conditions.

Owen continued his development. A few months later, at the end of his senior-year track season, he placed second at the Shore Conference two mile, being outkicked down the home stretch by one of his fiercest rivals, Chris Horel from Christian Brothers Academy, but improving his two-mile time to 9:31. The next day, in typical OB1 fashion, he returned the favor, this time outkicking Horel to win the Shore Conference mile. Owen concluded his high school career and our coach-athlete relationship by going all the way to the New Jersey State Meet of Champions and acquitting himself as he always does with dignity and aplomb in the two mile.

Owen at the time of writing is loving life at Georgetown University where he remains a dedicated runner and integral member of the cross-country and track teams and is about to begin his sophomore year.

In summary, Owen B. was the classic example of the diamond in the rough.

He was quiet and unassuming at the outset, and I had no idea of the talent and dedication that were to unfold over the next two years. If there was ever proof positive of the slogan do not judge a book by its cover, then Owen would be this slogan personified.

Upon reflection, I now understand that Owen "Just got it." Blessed with an unswerving desire and passion to succeed in the lowest-key manner possible, he understood the short- and long-term plans. He understood what we were trying to accomplish with each workout. He understood the essential aspects of sequential, progressive training incorporating the correct amounts of strength, speed endurance, and pure speed in conjunction with a well-balanced lifestyle incorporating appropriate levels of rest and sleep, proper nutrition, hydration, and attention to range of motion and flexibility. In short, he is the consummate athlete, willing to trust in his coach but at the same time not afraid to ask questions in order to increase his own knowledge and understanding. He understands the concept of optimal stress followed by optimal recovery equaling optimal performance.

He is a blue-collar athlete with incredible work ethic, and I am proudest of the fact that he always followed my running advice to *walk quietly and carry a big stick!*

CHAPTER 13

Reflections
of a Coach

Running is an extraordinary combination of physics and biology that produces one of the most amazing phenomena in evolution: the artistry and poetry in motion of the living creature. Unlike the crude machines that humans create, there are no squeaks, no rattles, no grinding of artificial materials.

In the context of running as a sport, the phrase "getting out of trouble" refers specifically to the effective management of difficulty and discomfort brought on by physiological and/or psychological stress.

Examples of physiological stress are

1. running too fast and out of control, causing a rapid deterioration in the working ability to complete the task at hand;
2. lacking fuel or hydration at the end of a long run;
3. running uphill;
4. running in adverse weather conditions such as heat, cold, humidity, or high winds.

Examples of psychological stress or difficulty are

1. awareness of slowing down;
2. fear of slowing down;
3. negative thinking, lack of motivation to continue, wanting to quit;
4. increasing anxiety from physical discomfort;

5. fear of the remaining distance in run or race;

6. mental fatigue.

These are just a few examples. We all have our own particular demons in this area, so please feel free to add yours to the list. Basically, anytime our running is negatively affected, we can consider ourselves to be in trouble.

After we take a closer look at some of the difficulties we might face in our daily runs, we will return to my Fab Four, my tried and true methods designed to enhance relaxation, increase efficiency, and most important, to help get you out of trouble when trouble arrives. Once you have successfully employed these methods, you will find that they can serve not only to improve the psychological aspect of your runs but also to increase your motivation to get out the door, confident in the knowledge that you will be better equipped to deal with discomfort when it comes along.

Running In or Out of Trouble?

For the human body to achieve locomotion, thousands of occurrences take place every second, a complex sequence of events that culminates in seamless movement.

The faster the pace in running, the more intense and frenetic are the behind-the-scenes physiological actions required to create forward movement. Yet often up to a point, the faster the running, the more relaxed the runner may appear to the observer, particularly a very talented runner in the early stages of a workout or race.

How can this be? There are several possible reasons.

Internally, when at an accelerated pace, the human body is performing at very high intensity. The heart and lungs are pumping at or close to maximum capacity, the central nervous system is at full voltage, the muscles are rapidly contracting and expanding, and the bones are moving fast. At this higher speed, there is a heightened state of awareness. Subconsciously, the body performs all the necessary functions more efficiently than usual, and for a short time the runner can become more efficient without even realizing it and appear to be more relaxed at speed. The essence of this book has been to teach you to *consciously* make these changes in order to permanently enhance your running.

Running can be a very challenging sport. It is fun, yes, but fun in a very strange way. How else can you explain a sport that keeps you looking forward to your run all day, but when you finally experience it keeps you looking at your watch because you can't wait for it to end? I am not suggesting that every run is like this, but if you are honest with yourself, you will agree that quite a few fall into this category.

The love/hate relationship that most if not all of us share with running is perhaps a testament to its difficulty as a sport. Quite often, making the decision to head out the door to your local park, trail, road, mountain range, beach, or track is the hardest commitment to make. I am not sure that athletes in many other sports experience the constant mind games that are associated with our everyday running. I know that swimmers, cyclists, and triathletes, among others, experience these same emotions. Many other athletes, however, do not. Soccer, tennis, or golf enthusiasts, to name a few, do not have to bribe themselves to get out the door in order to participate in their favorite sport on a regular basis.

Again, I am not suggesting for one second that these sports do not require nerves or create butterflies in their players, as they most certainly do. The difference is the anguish and anticipation that runners experience in connection with the physical and psychological pain that running often produces. After all, every day that we run, we are challenged to overcome both physical and mental obstacles. These obstacles vary in degree of difficulty. While the motion or movement of running is linear, the physiological and psychological aspects are definitely not.

A fascinating aspect to running and one that produces a strong kindred spirit among its participants is that no one is excluded from difficulty. The pains are not restricted to the hard efforts of a track workout or race, and it is just as common for an elite runner in peak racing shape to feel miserable during an everyday recovery run as runners at the novice or intermediate level. Continuing in this vein, just how is it that on a run-of-the-mill, midweek five-miler at two minutes per mile slower than our current 10K race pace, we feel worse than we did the previous weekend racing in a local 10K at that two-minute-per-mile faster pace?

While many of these difficult running days can be attributed to poor nutrition, inadequate hydration, sleep deprivation, and other physical limitations or restrictions, I also believe that the answer lies somewhere deep in the mysterious magic of this ancient sport.

As difficult as running can sometimes be, it can also be an effortless, flowing, relaxing, and euphoric symphony of movement. These types of runs, when we are firing on all cylinders, are usually all too infrequent. As runners, our attempts to get in the zone closely resemble a search for the Holy Grail. Why is it, then, that a sport that has so many participants and that can at times be so utterly torturous has prompted so few people to work on improving their form and biomechanics? Strange too is the fact that in comparison with cardiovascular/pulmonary developmental books or training guides, very little has even been written on the subject of running biomechanics.

Golf and tennis represent only two of the many sports whose enthusiasts are willing to invest a great deal of time in working on their game by learning, practicing, and perfecting the fundamentals. Yet runners, for the most part, remain oblivious to the tremendous improvements to be gained through developing and refining their biomechanical proficiency.

I am not alluding to the hard tempo, fartlek, long runs, and track workouts that you do. I am referencing the very essence of physically moving your body step-by-step across the ground. This is the biomechanics of running, the contraction of the muscles required to facilitate the optimal forward movement of your skeletal system.

Coach GP's Fab Four: A review

Let's return to my Fab Four, as detailed at the end of key chapters in this book. I am not suggesting that once you incorporate these four elements into your running it will all be easy from there. Far from it. However, they will provide the necessary tools to get you home or to the end of your race. (If nothing else, they will keep your mind occupied and those negative thoughts at bay.) The Fab Four will get you out of trouble.

Fab #1 RUN TALL

Whether you are on a neighborhood jog or a peak-season race, the taller you are relative to your own height, the better your running will be. You must get your hips up. The jockey must sit atop the horse with proper upright posture.

Fab #2 FOOT STRIKE

With proper foot strike, you will be better able to generate drive-off force with your takeoff leg, therefore maintaining your preferred flight time. This in turn allows three more things to happen:

1. You will have precious extra milliseconds in flight for your working muscles to relax.
2. The longer flight time will result in a more complete leg cycle. The front foot will be able to land closer to a point directly below your center of gravity (helping you remain taller).
3. The improved drive-off also results in faster foot speed, bringing the heel up behind the body (closer to your hips, remember met-

ronome, weight closer to point of axis!) and providing a faster, smoother leg action. This in turn generates more speed, the speed helps your flight time, and thus the cycle continues.

Fab #3 ARM DRIVE

It is impossible to maintain efficient running biomechanics (maximal flight time) without proper arm drive. The arm drive provides the counterthrust to help drive the lead leg of the corresponding side with enough lift and force to fly through the air in an optimal manner. How do you know what that optimal manner is? You don't have to, because during the course of your training runs—runs that are performed at specific, accurate paces—your arm drive will develop its own optimal cadence for a given pace. All that is left for you to do is to start your races or training runs at the right pace for your given distance and maintain the arm drive that your arms set for themselves at the beginning of the run.

Fab #4 BREATHING

It is essential during times of difficulty, be they physiological or psychological, that you get in sync with your body's natural breathing rhythm and run to that rhythm or cadence. The horse and jockey must be at one with each other. Pay attention, and you will notice that your breathing rhythm keeps time with your foot strike. This is a very powerful safety net, and it will keep you more relaxed and inwardly focused, taking your mind away from negative thoughts and ideas. Your breathing rhythm is the conductor keeping time in a tremendous cascading symphony.

Running is a very simple and enjoyable sport, but it can turn very challenging when trouble strikes. Applying the Fab Four will ensure that you are well equipped to handle difficulties as they arise. There are many components to a well-balanced training program, but in the sport of running, unless the integrity of your musculoskeletal system is well-maintained, it is just a matter of time before your performance is compromised.

Final Thoughts

In the past, coaching and other popular sources of running information have focused almost exclusively on the cardiopulmonary aspects of training. This old-fashioned approach is slowly giving way to the ideas that form follows function and that function can be changed with skillful assessment, redirection, and teaching. There is a skill to running that can be practiced and honed over time.

Prior to the 1970s, coaching was mainly restricted to elite runners. The recreational boom had yet to take place. From the mid-1970s to the mid-1990s, coaching began to reach a wider audience and clubs began forming across the United States. Coaching was for the most part performed by former elite runners from the high school, college, or professional ranks. These coaches may have received some instruction in biomechanics, but more often than not, they worked from a more-running-is-better philosophy. Thousands of new recreational runners took up this philosophy and subsequently followed this method in their own training.

It was not long before an explosion of recreational sports injuries occurred, an increase that the medical profession has struggled to handle. The result of this new wave of injuries? Whole new areas of health care known collectively as sports medicine.

In the early part of the 21st century, as major marathons and other races continue to grow, high-quality coaching is more important than ever. Often inspired by charity organizations or friends or relatives who have completed a race, more and more people are taking to running for the first time.

Certain members of the medical profession maintain that running is bad for you or that it causes injuries. This is far from true. Poor biomechanics and an inferior musculoskeletal system are what lead to running injuries.

I do not deny that a certain section of the human population is predisposed genetically that would make it advisable for them to consider a different sport, perhaps one that is not load bearing such as swimming or cycling. This notwithstanding, all others can benefit greatly from a solid foundation of professional coaching on how to be a well-balanced athlete. Coaching would include instruction in progressive training with optimal recovery time, range of motion and flexibility, nutrition and hydration, and sufficient hours of rest and sleep.

Of prime importance would be instruction in the art of proper running biomechanics to ensure that you are moving your body through space in the most economical, efficient, and powerful manner possible.

Remember, run to the maximum height relative to your own height. In short, "Run Tall, Run Easy."

See you on the roads and trails.

Coach GP

CHAPTER 14

Life in the Fast Lane

Ears, shoulders, elbows, and hips in perfect alignment.

The buck stops here!

A young runner must be developed, not used.

Strong lead leg, knee drive, and proper extension of the ankle at the point of takeoff.

The second law of running bio-mechanics, optimal distance in flight.

The responsibility of coaching is no joke.

Focus and concentration are essential components for the competitive runner!

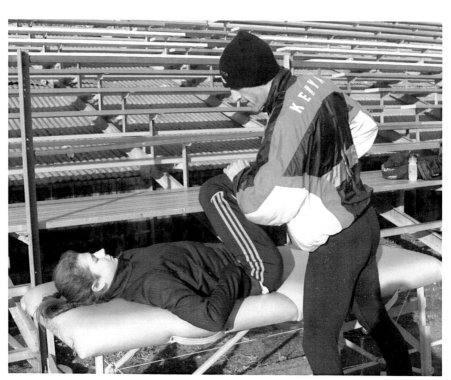

Active isolated stretching pre- and postworkout is recommended.

A coach in focus.

Even a hard training session
requires some lighter moments!

Man, those tunes are loud!

Practicing the side float drill places the foot in the perfect ground contact position.

Group track training—the sum is greater than the parts!

I told you it was a hard training session!

Running drills are awesome. Perfect practice makes perfect.

Running drills make for a perfect dynamic warm-up on a cool winter morning.

Jersey Stinger coaching staff: Coach Tom Schaefer (left), Coach GP (middle), and Coach John Cancro (right).

About the Author

In November 1990 Gerard "GP" Pearlberg ran the New York City Marathon in 4:41. It would prove to be a race that would change his career and his life.

A successful athlete in school, GP was determined to find out why running the marathon had been such a difficult challenge. Since that day he has made it his mission to uncover the secrets to moving one's body across the earth with as much efficiency, economy, and speed as possible.

Over the next 17 years, although considering himself athletically suited to middle-distance events, GP ran 23 marathons, including 14 in less than three hours and a 2:34 at the 1998 Napa Valley Marathon. In the 1998 Nike World Games, GP won the gold medal in the 1,500 meters for the 35 to 39 year age group and ran a 4:21 road mile and a 4:01 1,500 meters on the track.

Competing as a masters runner from 2003 to 2007, GP earned multiple USATF All-American status at the 800 and 1,500 meter distances.

GP returned to the New York City Marathon in 1996, this time running a 2:42. His unique research on running biomechanics and the fascinating lessons that led to his having shaved nearly two hours off his previous New York City Marathon time are shared with you in this second edition of *Run Tall, Run Easy: The Ultimate Guide to Better Running Mechanics*.

GP has been coaching professionally since 1995 and has been a certified USA Track & Field coach since January 1997. He has coached, counseled, listened to, and learned from thousands of runners, both professional and amateur, from all over the world.

He was cofounder of the Iron Maidens all-women's running group in Santa Cruz, California, and is the cofounder of the online coaching company RunningBuzz.com, LLC.

GP uses his high degree of energy to provide TV commentary, start-finish line announcing, and running seminars at races and running events across North and South America.

Born and raised in England, GP now lives at the New Jersey Shore, USA. Recently retired from racing to focus more on his family and career, GP still trains hard with his high school and collegiate athletes throughout the year.

His passions are people, travel, surfing, and Chelsea FC; and at the center of his universe are his two young sons, Luke and Sam.

More Praise for *Run Tall, Run Easy,* Second Edition

"Coach GP has done it again! I've seen him at running expos around the country talking to people about *Run Tall, Run Easy.* Now with all of Coach GP's information in one book, it will be much easier for people to Run Tall, Run Easy all the time!

"Written in a form that even the beginning runner will understand, I'm sure that runners of every caliber—from the casual runner to the world class—will benefit from this wonderful book.

"I'm now a masters runner and I'm running taller and easier than I have in years! Coach GP's 'Fab Four' have re-energized my running. His book is a must-read for all runners."

—Dick Beardsley,
2:08:53 marathoner,
the fifth-fastest time
in U.S. men's marathon
history; two-time Grandma's
Marathon champion and
current course
record holder